'Betrothed to mad!'

'Perhaps I didn't ph[?]
need to marry me, [?]
for a short time,' he explained. 'I am in need of a temporary fiancée.'

'But why me? We do not deal at all well together.'

'The strong aversion you've shown for my company suits me very well, I've no doubt you will be quite willing to cry off at the appropriate time. You want your brother's estate back—it will be done. Is a few months in my company such a sacrifice for your brother?'

'A few months! I'd rather spend an eternity in hell than a day in your company.'

Ann Elizabeth Cree is married and lives in Boise, Idaho, with her family. She has worked as a nutritionist and an accountant. Her favourite form of daydreaming has always been weaving romantic stories in her head. With the encouragement of a friend, she started putting those stories to paper. In addition to writing, and caring for two lively boys, two cats and two dogs, she enjoys gardening, playing the piano, and, of course, reading.

A BARGAIN
WITH FATE

Ann Elizabeth Cree

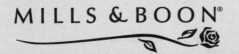

MILLS & BOON®

MILLS & BOON and MILLS & BOON with the Rose Device are registered trademarks of the publisher.

First published in Great Britain 1998
Harlequin Mills & Boon Limited,
Eton House, 18-24 Paradise Road, Richmond, Surrey TW9 1SR

© Annemarie Hasnain 1998

ISBN 0 263 81236 7

Set in Times Roman 10½ on 12 pt.
04-9811-71713 C1

Printed and bound in Great Britain
by Caledonian International Book Manufacturing Ltd, Glasgow

Chapter One

Whatever was taking the man so long? Rosalyn, Lady Jeffreys pushed a strand of hair off her brow with nervous fingers. She hoped Lord Stamford would soon put in an appearance, or she would be tempted to flee from his house like a common thief.

She had spent the entire morning mustering up the courage to come. If she possessed an ounce of sense, she would have turned coward and jumped back into the hackney carriage the minute she laid eyes on the imposing mansion in St James's Square. Instead, she'd marched up the front steps, determined to confront the notorious Marquis of Stamford.

To her dismay, Lord Stamford's butler not only indicated his lordship would return shortly but insisted on showing her into this intimidating drawing room with its pale green walls and a fireplace with the most elaborate carving she'd ever seen.

The butler had been surprisingly solicitous for such a stiff, dignified man, inquiring if she were warm enough and insisting on arranging her chair near the hearth. She had had some idea that a man of Lord

Stamford's stamp would run a household as wild as his reputation. Instead, the few servants she'd spotted looked respectable enough and went quietly about their business. The drawing room showed no signs of haphazard management. It was furnished in the height of elegance: the mahogany chairs polished to perfection, rich Oriental rugs scattered about the floor. Above the elaborately carved mantelpiece was the portrait of a darkly handsome man, his hair tied back with a riband, his hand on a sword, his cool gaze resting on Rosalyn with a mocking expression.

Rosalyn shifted uneasily. The house seemed unnaturally quiet. She heard no footsteps, no servants' voices—only the relentless ticking of the clock. Another five minutes dragged by. It was quite apparent Lord Stamford did not intend to see her. She was miffed. Rudeness obviously numbered among his many other shortcomings.

Well, she could not sit here forever. She would have to hunt the man down and force him to see her. She stood up so abruptly her reticule slid to the ground. Its contents spilled across the floor.

'Oh, drat!' Rosalyn exclaimed. As she knelt on the carpet, the poke of her bonnet hit the edge of the chair, which knocked it askew. Tears of frustration sprang to her eyes. Could anything else possibly go wrong?

'Lady Jeffreys?'

A pair of shiny black riding boots appeared in her line of vision. She froze. Her horrified eyes travelled up a pair of lean, muscled thighs encased in buckskin breeches, over a dark riding coat covering a broad masculine chest and came to rest on the most wickedly handsome face she had seen in her life. With his lean, dark features and midnight black hair, he could be an arrogant Italian nobleman from a Gothic romance.

His disconcerting gaze swept over her face. She flushed and dropped her eyes. Her fingers trembled as she pushed her bonnet back into place. Never had she felt at such an utter disadvantage.

'It appears you need some help. May I be of assistance?' the man inquired politely.

'No, I…' She snapped into motion, grabbed the last item and shoved it into her reticule. She started to rise, but before she could protest, the man reached down and hauled her to her feet. She backed away, even more flustered.

A small smile of amusement quirked his lips. 'I am Stamford.'

'Lord Stamford?' This man could not possibly be the dissolute gamester she'd expected. Well above average height, his athletic figure proclaimed a man who spent more time in sporting pursuits than hovering around a gaming table. No lines of dissipation marred his fine aristocratic face. But most unexpected of all were the lines of humour lurking about his firm mouth.

Colour flooded her cheeks as the Marquis raised a curious brow.

'Perhaps you expected someone else? You look rather astounded.'

'I was merely surprised. I…I did not hear you come in, my lord.'

'You did seem to be occupied. I am sorry I kept you waiting so long. I usually ride in the mornings and had just returned when I was told you were here. I was not expecting visitors. Have we met before?'

His eyes flickered over her face in a coolly amused manner calculated to put her firmly in her place.

She raised her chin. 'No, we have not, my lord.'

'So you do not intend to claim an acquaintance with me?'

'No, why should I? I had not even heard of you until a few days ago.'

'The last lady unknown to me who called on me in this fashion wished to renew an acquaintance which I fear I did not recollect,' he informed her blandly.

Rosalyn stared at him. Whatever was he talking about? Then a shaft of anger shot through her as she perceived his meaning. Did he really have the audacity to imagine she had called on some flimsy pretext merely to make his acquaintance?

Suppressing the desire to let him know exactly what she thought of such arrogance, she said, 'I am not here on a social call but on a matter of business, my lord. There is no other reason I would ever wish to call on you.'

'I beg your pardon, my lady. I usually deal through my agent in business matters. However, in this case…' his lazy gaze slid over her face and down her body '…I shall be delighted to make an exception.'

Her cheeks grew even warmer. She hated her appalling tendency to blush. 'This is a personal matter.'

His dark brows raised a fraction. 'A personal matter? Now I am curious, Lady Jeffreys—especially since you say we have never met.'

'It is not my personal business. It is my brother's.'

'Your brother's?' Surprise flitted across his features. He motioned towards the elegant brocade settee with a careless hand. 'Please be seated and tell me how I can help you.'

He settled his frame in one of the upholstered mahogany chairs arranged near the settee, his dark eyes fixed on her face.

'I am the sister of James Whitcomb,' she began, folding her hands tightly together, wishing he would not stare at her so. 'I believe you know him.'

'I made his acquaintance only a few days ago. Go on.'

'I know that he has lost his estate to you at cards.'

He stretched his muscular legs in front of him and crossed his arms over his chest. Although his expression was still that of the polite host, his eyes hardened almost imperceptibly. 'So, you are here at your brother's request?'

'No, of course not! He would be furious with me if he knew I was here. I pray you will never mention this to him!'

'I wouldn't think of it. I cannot see what business this is of yours, however.'

'What do you mean by that? Of course this affair is my business. He is my brother. It is our family estate!'

'I understood your brother has full title to the property and is free to do with it as he wishes.'

'That is true, of course, but I cannot sit by and watch it lost like this! I think it's quite despicable for you to take away someone's inheritance in such a shabby fashion!'

'Are you perchance implying I cheated, my lady?'

Rosalyn shifted uneasily under his hard gaze. 'No, I don't know that at all! I only meant that it was quite

wrong of you to take advantage of such a green boy!
I think that—'

'I appreciate your sisterly concern,' he drawled.
'But your brother is hardly a young boy. He was not
forced into staking his estate. I did not hold a pistol
to his head. He had no business playing for such high
stakes if he could not cover them. I am sorry about
the loss of your family estate, but I cannot do anything
about it.'

Cold fury seeped through her. 'I cannot imagine
why you would want another estate. I am certain you
must have quite enough.'

Lord Stamford laughed sardonically. He uncrossed
his arms and rose from his chair to lounge against the
carved marble chimney piece. He idly picked up one
of the small ivory figurines adorning the mantel. 'Can
one ever have enough estates? I am certain I can think
of something to do with the property. But I am still at
a loss to know exactly what you hoped to accomplish
by coming here today.' He returned the figurine to its
place and regarded her with cool indifference.

Rosalyn had never detested anyone more in her life.
She swallowed her anger, forcing herself to remain
calm. 'I had hoped we could reach some sort of agreement. I cannot pay you the entire price, but I am willing…'

She faltered as a cold, cynical light leapt to his eyes.
His gaze, suddenly insolent, raked her face and moved
appraisingly down her body, resting for an instant on
the soft curve of her breast. She sat frozen. No man,
not even her husband, had ever stared at her in such
a manner.

'An agreement? Exactly what sort of agreement did

you have in mind, my dear lady? I usually don't bargain my gambling debts away, but I am certain you and I could come to an arrangement that would satisfy both of us. You are not quite in my usual taste, but your figure is satisfactory and you are…pretty enough.'

'I beg your pardon?' For the second time, he'd managed to thoroughly confuse her.

Then his insulting words pierced her consciousness. Humiliation followed by pure outrage washed over her.

She shot to her feet. Her voice shook with suppressed fury. 'You think I am here to offer you…that? I would never do such a degrading thing. I would rather spend my life in debtor's prison or…or hang than come to such a despicable agreement with you!'

She whirled around and swept towards the door. But Stamford reached the door before her; his strong fingers closed over her wrist.

More than a little frightened, she tried to jerk her hand out of his iron grasp. His intimidating nearness, and the warmth of his hand, caused her heart to pound most alarmingly. She could smell the masculine scent of his cologne.

He could not possibly intend to ravish her now! Helplessly, she stared up into his dark compelling eyes surrounded by lashes far longer than any man's should be. His expression, so cold and sardonic only minutes before, was now warm with amusement.

'Please do not leave yet, Lady Jeffreys. I must offer my most sincere apologies and humbly beg your pardon. I am afraid I misunderstood your intentions. You must give me a chance to redeem myself by telling me what you wanted.' The laughter in his eyes rendered him dangerously attractive.

Her breath caught in her throat. 'I...I must go. Please release me, my lord.'

He instantly dropped her wrist. Gentle fingers caught her chin, tilting her face so he could look into her eyes. 'Don't look so frightened. I promise I won't seduce you in my drawing room. It's not good *ton*, you know.'

How dare he laugh at her after making such an improper suggestion? She slapped his hand away and glared at him. 'I have nothing more to say to you.'

He moved in front of her and rested his broad shoulders against the door and folded his arms over his chest. 'I won't let you go until you tell me what you wanted. I must make up for my despicable behaviour.'

'I cannot say you are behaving any better now,' she snapped.

His eyes danced, totally unrepentant. 'I am afraid I generally don't behave very well. More than one lady of my acquaintance has informed me of that very fact. But please tell me your request.' His mouth curved in a most devastating smile.

She flushed, resenting the implication that he categorised her with all the other women he knew, particularly as she could imagine the sort of female company he kept. But further argument appeared fruitless. He obviously had no intention of letting her go until she did as he bade her. Her shoulders slumped.

'I wanted to discuss some sort of arrangement to pay my brother's debt to you and ask you to return Meryton. I cannot pay you what it is worth, but I can pay something. I have an income from my husband

and a small house in London at my disposal. I should like to pay the debt off in instalments…with interest, of course.'

The laughter left his eyes. He said quietly, 'I am sorry, but I cannot fulfil your request, my lady.'

Disappointment surged through her. 'Why not?'

He shrugged. 'The debt is between your brother and me. I do not think he would appreciate your interference. If you wish to come to some sort of an arrangement with him, he may approach me. I would be willing to consider it, but I cannot promise to restore the estate to him.'

'I see.' She prayed she would not burst into tears. 'Please allow me to leave.'

He paused with his hand on the doorknob, the plain gold signet ring he wore reflecting the sunlight filtering in through the brocade curtains. 'Tell me, do you also have a passion for gambling, Lady Jeffreys?'

'Of course not. I am the worst card player in the world.'

He laughed gently. 'It's too bad others are not as honest about their abilities as you.'

He opened the door. She moved past him, ignoring the arm he held out to her. She hastened down the curving staircase to the hallway. His butler sprang to open the door. To her vexation, Lord Stamford trailed her down the steps and followed her to the waiting hackney carriage.

'Are you in London often, Lady Jeffreys?' he asked conversationally as if nothing had passed between them.

'Rarely,' she replied without looking at him.

He leaned towards her, the sun glinting off his raven

hair. 'I thought not. Then you should know it's most improper of you to call on me in this fashion,' he said kindly, but his eyes danced. 'I am surprised your husband allowed it.'

'Not that it is any of your business, my lord, but I am a widow, not a young girl. I can do what I please.'

'Perhaps so, but you should have at least brought a maid with you. My reputation is not the most sterling. Respectable ladies know better than to call on me and certainly not unchaperoned.'

Completely taken aback, she stammered, 'I...I trusted you would behave like a gentleman.'

He grinned at her in a maddening fashion. 'I am afraid you sadly misplaced your trust. I am no gentleman.'

'That's nothing to boast about,' she replied tartly.

'I look forward to our next meeting, Lady Jeffreys.' Without removing his eyes from her face, he captured her hand and raised it to his lips.

Rosalyn jerked her hand away. 'Since I do not move in the same dissipated circles as you, there is not likely to be another meeting.'

He looked startled at that but quickly recovered. 'Shall we make a wager on that, my lady? I think we shall meet again—and soon.'

'Goodbye, my lord,' she said. He merely smiled in his infuriating way and insisted on handing her into the coach.

Rosalyn settled back into the hard cushions. How she wished she were a man! Planting him a facer or, better yet, running him through with a sword would give her unbounded satisfaction.

Her anger quickly gave away to depression. She had

completely failed in her mission. James was no better off; their home had been lost to a stranger. A tear trickled down her cheek, quickly followed by another. She fumbled in her reticule for her handkerchief, grateful she had been too angry to cry in front of the abominable Lord Stamford.

'Oh dear,' she whispered. Could this day possibly get any worse? Her favourite fan was missing, undoubtedly lying in Lord Stamford's elegant drawing room.

'Damn!' Michael muttered as he entered his study. He threw his long frame into the chair in front of his desk, a frown marring his brow. The whole business of this estate was proving to be a blasted nuisance. He'd never meant to gamble Whitcomb out of his estate, but the chance to foil Edmund Fairchilde, a man he disliked, was too tempting. And in spite of himself, he'd felt a flash of pity for the young man, clearly in over his head and about to be ruined, which he surely would be if he fell in Fairchilde's clutches.

To complicate matters, he discovered the Dowager Countess of Carlyn was James Whitcomb's maternal grandmother. Lady Carlyn was a friend of his aunt, Lady Spence. Michael could quite imagine his aunt's words upon learning her nephew had gambled Whitcomb out of his estate. They would hardly be complimentary to Michael's character.

And now Lady Jeffreys. What in the devil possessed him to insult her in such a fashion? He had known the instant he first looked into her sweet face and clear honest eyes, her bonnet charmingly askew, that she was a lady in every respect.

He spent too much time with the *demimonde*, rendering him far too cynical. Most women of his acquaintance would have no compunction in trading their charms to pay off a gambling debt. It would not have been the first time he had been made such an offer.

He rose, a slight smile lifting the corners of his mouth. He reluctantly admitted she interested him despite her very real dislike for him. She was quite lovely in a quiet sort of way. Her prim grey gown could not completely disguise the soft curves of her breast and hips or detract from her luxuriant chestnut hair and large hazel eyes. Michael quite looked forward to their next meeting, although she would most likely cut him dead, as he undoubtedly deserved.

His thoughts were interrupted by the soft cough of Watkins, his butler, hovering in the doorway. 'M'lord.'

'What is it, Watkins? Not another unexpected visitor, I trust.'

A feminine voice spoke from behind the butler. 'I shall show myself in. I do not wish to be told again that my nephew is not at home.'

Michael inwardly groaned as Lady Margaret Spence swept into the room, a determined look on her aristocratic face. He wished Lady Jeffreys to the devil for her ill-timed visit. He should have been at White's by now and out of reach of his aunt and her unwelcome business.

He bowed over Lady Spence's gloved hand. 'My dear aunt, I am delighted to see you,' he murmured.

Lady Spence fixed intelligent blue eyes on her nephew's face. 'I doubt it. This is the first time I've managed to catch you at home. I am almost inclined to think you're avoiding me.'

She drew off her kidskin gloves in a businesslike manner and seated herself in the chair near his desk. In her mid-fifties, she possessed the figure and posture of a much younger woman. Today, she was fashionably dressed in a powder-blue round gown with a matching pelisse which set off her greying blonde hair becomingly.

Michael seated himself on the other side of his desk. 'Why would I wish to avoid you? You know I am always pleased to see you. And how is my uncle? I have not yet seen him about town.'

'Frederick is quite well. However, I did not call to exchange pleasantries with you. You know very well why I am here, Michael, so I suggest you stop fencing with me. You cannot avoid this discussion forever.' She impaled him with ice-blue eyes. He sunk back in his chair with all the enthusiasm of a fox run to ground by a pack of hounds.

Nearly an hour later Michael entered the portals of White's. He was shown to a table in the corner of the dining room where he was greeted by a stocky blond man attired in a bottle-green coat and striped waistcoat, his starched cravat elaborately tied in an oriental knot.

'Michael, my boy!' the gentleman exclaimed. 'I thought you weren't going to show. I've nearly starved waiting for you and was forced to order.'

Michael glanced at his cousin's ample figure and laughed. 'I don't think there's too much danger of that, Charles,' he said pulling up a chair. 'I've been besieged by visitors today. First I had a call from—' he broke off, frowning. 'Never mind. The last caller was my Aunt Margaret.'

'Been after you again about that chit? You'll end up with your neck in the parson's noose before you know it. I'm glad your Aunt Margaret ain't my relative. Don't envy you your father either.'

'They're bad enough apart, but together—I'd rather face a firing squad. I'd have much better odds.' Michael frowned at the glass of dry sherry the waiter set in front of him. 'My aunt came to inform me my bride-to-be will arrive in town within a fortnight. There's been a slight illness in the family that prevents her from coming any sooner. I'll have a reprieve at any rate.'

'Don't see how they can force you into marriage. Good lord, you're thirty, well past your majority,' Charles said.

'Well, would you care to oppose my father?'

'Good point,' said Charles hastily as the waiter brought his meal. 'Don't know how anyone could oppose your parent when he fixes you with that damned devilish stare. Sets me to quaking in my boots every time. I'd marry a woman with a horse-face and freckles before crossing swords with Eversleigh.'

There was silence for a few moments while Charles dove into his food with all the vigour of a man who hadn't eaten for weeks. Michael sipped his sherry in contemplative silence, his long legs stretched out in front of him.

His father, the Duke of Eversleigh, was notorious for his iron-fisted management of his family's personal affairs. Several weeks ago he had summoned Michael to Eversleigh Hall. There, in his formidable study, the Duke had coolly informed his heir it was time he married. Since his son did not seem capable of choosing a suitable bride for himself, a bride had been chosen for him. The young lady was Miss Helena Randall, the granddaughter of a long-standing friend. She was to be presented at Court this season. After a suitable period, unless there were major objections on the part of either party, their betrothal would be announced.

Michael could see any number of objections, starting with the fact he had no desire to marry a girl fresh out of the schoolroom. Argument with his father appeared useless. The Duke wore the implacable expression that meant he'd made up his mind and would brook no opposition. In addition, the Duke's health was poor due to a recent severe bout of pneumonia that nearly claimed his life. Michael hesitated to come to cuffs with his father in his still-weakened condition.

Charles, who always thought better on a satisfied stomach, dropped his fork with a clatter. 'What you need, my boy, is a fiancée!'

Michael eyed him as if he had taken leave of his senses. 'Exactly what I'll end up with if my father has his way. That's what I'm trying to avoid.'

'Would save you a lot of trouble,' said Charles earnestly with all the experience of a happily betrothed man. 'Now that I'm betrothed to Beth I never worry about matchmaking mothers trying to foist their daughters on me. Not that I've ever had the number you've had. No more hounding from my mother about finding a suitable wife. And Beth's a good girl; doesn't have odd fits or expect me to escort her to any of those damned musical evenings.'

Michael was fascinated. 'I never realised there were so many advantages attached to a betrothal.'

'Well, the point is, Michael, if you were already betrothed your family could hardly expect you to offer for Miss Randall.'

'Very true. It would be awkward. But the problem with fiancées is that one is expected to marry them.'

Charles downed several slices of ham, his brow creased in thought. He wiped his mouth on his napkin and looked up. 'You could hire one.'

'Hire one? One what?'

'A fiancée! Remember when Greely hired an actress to be his wife so he could inherit from his old uncle in Manchester or some other ungodly place? Worked too; the old man fell for it and Greely got the money. Dare say he had to pay that actress a bundle.'

Michael grinned. A few of the actresses he knew flashed across his mind.

'That may work very well in Manchester but hardly in London. Where in the world would I find an actress I could hope to pass off in the middle of a London season as my fiancée? Even the best of them couldn't appear respectable enough to suit my father. Besides, my aunt could sniff out an impostor at ten paces!'

'Maybe you could find a foreign actress.'

'Good God, no! My father would be in a rare temper if I announced my engagement to a foreign woman! Don't trouble yourself, I'll figure out a way to avoid this entanglement. I always do.' He polished off his sherry. 'Where are you off to tonight, Charles?'

'To Lady Winthrope's rout. Probably another one of her damned squeezes. Promised to escort my mother and Beth. How about you?'

'I'll put in an appearance.'

'I've heard Elinor Marchant is in town,' said Charles carefully. 'Have you met her yet?'

'Today, while riding in the park. She was determined to regale me with every bit of gossip she could think of, half of it probably unfounded rumour.'

'Hope you don't plan to take up with her again.' Charles shuddered. 'Never saw such a temper in my life. Don't know how you could have put up with it. That last scene—right in the middle of a ball! Heaving vases around!'

A grin lit up Michael's face. 'Only one vase. And it wasn't in the middle of a ball, merely in a private room.'

'One vase, half a dozen vases, what does it matter? You're well rid of her! Never know how you manage to come up with these vixens. Need to show a bit more discrimination in the petticoat line.'

Michael laughed and rose from the table in a lazy movement. 'Put your mind to rest, Charles. I have no interest in renewing a relationship with Lady Marchant. Ready to go? There's a pair of chestnuts up for auction at Tattersall's I've been wanting to see.'

Michael only half-attended to his cousin's conversation as they made their way to the auction yard. Instead, he found himself thinking of Lady Jeffreys. Would she be present at Lady Winthrope's rout? He hoped so, for he had the perfect excuse for speaking to her. After his aunt had departed, Watkins had presented him with a small folded fan, saying he believed it belonged to the young lady. Michael had taken the fan, assuring Watkins he would personally see it was returned to its owner.

Chapter Two

'I was sorry to hear of your brother's troubles. I know how much Meryton means to you,' Edmund Fairchilde said softly. 'Perhaps there is something I could do to help.'

Rosalyn looked up into his cool, hooded eyes, and wished she could escape from him. However, it was impossible in Lady Winthrope's crowded drawing room unless she was to clamber over one of the guests behind her.

'Thank you, there is nothing you can do. But, how did you know? I had thought it was a private game.' She tried to keep the dismay from her voice. She had hoped no one outside of Lord Stamford, James and herself knew about the wager.

A faint smile touched his thin lips. 'I was also there, my lady. I had hoped there was something I could do, but alas, Stamford rarely loses. It makes one wonder…but, his temper, one hates to suggest… At any rate, do not worry, only the three of us were present, and I am very discreet.'

'Thank you.' She managed a smile, not certain she

trusted him at all. He had been a visitor to Meryton, coming down once with a group of her brother's friends. Although he had been charmingly courteous, there was something about his hooded gaze, particularly the way it sometimes rested on her, that made her uneasy.

'But I do wish to offer my help.' He smiled again. 'Before you protest, you must hear my proposal. I am not without resources, and I should hate to see you turned from your family home. Come driving with me tomorrow, and I shall tell you my proposition.'

'That is very kind, but I...I shall be busy tomorrow.'

'Will you? Then the next day.' His eyes rested on her face as if he wanted to calculate the impact of his words. 'I have longed for the opportunity to become better acquainted with you ever since I saw you at Meryton.'

'My dear, there you are!'

Relieved, she turned to see her grandmother, Lady Carlyn, suddenly appear next to her. Lady Carlyn acknowledged Fairchilde with a cool smile. 'If you will excuse us, sir, I must introduce my granddaughter to Lady Carruthers. I fear she is about to leave.' She dragged Rosalyn away, but not before Rosalyn saw Fairchilde's brows snap together in sudden anger.

Lady Carlyn marched Rosalyn from the drawing room to an adjoining room, then stopped. 'My dear, you should not be talking to Edmund Fairchilde. His reputation is, well, not quite what it should be. People will talk.'

'I didn't wish to talk with him. He approached me. He is an acquaintance of James's.'

'Indeed. I must say I am surprised at James, although he has been going about with some rather wild young men. I hope he will settle down soon enough and properly manage Meryton. It has been most careless of him to leave you to do so. Women have no business running estates.'

Rosalyn said nothing. She had not yet informed her grandmother that James had gambled away Meryton. For once she was thankful that her grandmother's mind tended to jump from subject to subject. 'However, we must concentrate on you. What did you think of Neville Hastings?'

'Neville Hastings?' Rosalyn finally recalled a plump, man with thinning hair and creaking corsets. Lady Carlyn had introduced him to her when they first arrived. 'He seemed very nice, I suppose.'

'A bit plump, although a diet of rice and water would help. But twenty thousand pounds a year, that is nothing to sneeze at in a husband.'

'A husband?'

'Why, yes, for you, my love.'

'Grandmama! I don't want a husband!'

'But of course you do. You are only six-and-twenty and still quite pretty. I must own Neville Hastings is not quite what I had in mind. Someone with a bit more dash.'

'I never plan to remarry.'

'Of course, it will be someone you like,' Lady Carlyn continued, paying no heed to Rosalyn as usual. 'I have several eligible men in mind.'

Her sharp grey eyes darted around the packed drawing room, seeking more prey. 'I see Lord Brandon has arrived. He is searching for a wife. A pity he has five children, but I know you are very fond...'

'Please, no! I am rather tired. I would like to rest for a few minutes.'

Lady Carlyn fidgeted with her fan, then snapped it shut. 'Very well. You may stay here. I must admit, you do look a trifle pale. No use having you faint, although Ellen Winthrope would consider that the highest compliment! I must have a few words with Maria Smythe-Howard and then we can leave.'

Rosalyn watched her grandmother make her way through the packed room, a small plump figure dressed in a gown of orange satin completely unsuitable for a woman of more advanced years. The dictates of fashion meant nothing to Lady Carlyn.

Rosalyn shifted uncomfortably. Her feet hurt from standing, her mouth ached from smiling, and her head pounded from the strain of making conversation in the impossible noise. There was no place to sit, as all the furniture had been removed to accommodate the several hundred people Lady Winthrope expected to parade through her rooms.

At least she was free of her grandmother for a few minutes. Lady Carlyn's unflagging energy was exhausting. And this hare-brained notion of finding her a husband...she had enough to distress her without fighting her grandmother's schemes.

Her thoughts turned to James, as they had all day. Ever since their mother's death, four years earlier, he'd become more and more unmanageable. She no longer knew how to reach him. Somehow, she had believed if she tried to preserve Meryton for him, he would return, for he had once loved Meryton as much as she did. Now Meryton was lost and, in her heart, she feared he was lost also.

'Oh!' She gasped as a stout gentlemen stepped back, jostling her with such force that she lost her balance and stumbled sideways against a tall, hard form. Strong hands caught her bare arms, causing an unexpected warmth to course through her.

'I beg your pardon,' she said in confusion.

'There is no need to apologise. I am always delighted when beautiful ladies fall into my arms.'

That familiar, detestable voice caused her heart to stop. Slowly, she lifted her head to meet the Marquis of Stamford's laughing eyes. For the briefest of moments, he seemed not to recognise her, and then, a wicked grin spread across his face.

'Why, Lady Jeffreys, what a delightful surprise to run into you like this. Particularly since you assured me we never moved in the same dissipated circles.'

She jerked away from him. Irritation replaced the unwelcome sensation she'd felt at his touch. 'Please excuse me, my lord.'

'But I have looked forward to seeing you all evening. You cannot mean to leave me now when I have finally found you.'

The hated colour flooded her face at the implication that he actually hoped to see her. Of course, she didn't believe it for a moment. 'I must find my grandmother. I do not have time for idle chatter.'

He laughed. 'Is there any other sort at these tedious affairs? But never mind, I wanted to see you for a particular reason. I have something for you.'

'Something for me?'

'Yes, your fan. I believe you dropped it in my drawing room. I wanted to return it to you.'

'You've been carrying my fan around?'

'In the remote chance I might see you.' He reached under his evening coat, towards his white embroidered waistcoat.

She nearly grabbed his hand. 'No, please, not here.' What would people think if they saw him pull a fan from his pocket and present it to her?

'Shall I call on you, then?'

'No! I mean, why can you not send it to me?'

'But I want to give it to you in person, to make certain you get it, of course. I was hoping we could become better acquainted.'

'I have no desire to become better acquainted with you, my lord.'

'But I would like the opportunity to change your mind.' A lazy half-smile, full of meaning, curled the edges of his mouth as he let his leisurely gaze travel over her person.

Mesmerised, she stared back. It occurred to her that his eyes were really not black at all, but the deepest, richest shade of brown she'd ever seen. And would his thick midnight hair, curling slightly at the nape of his neck, feel as soft and silky to her touch as it looked?

What was she thinking of?

'Never! You'll never change my mind!'

She whirled away, only to find her escape blocked by two ladies standing directly behind them. They gasped and stared, their fans stopped in mid-air. From the looks of pleasurable shock on their faces, she had little doubt they had heard her every word.

Lord Stamford nodded to the ladies, who tittered

and turned away. Grasping Rosalyn's arm, he bent his head towards her, and said conversationally, 'It's best not to pick a quarrel with me in public. It will hardly ease your entrée into society.'

Her mouth fell open. Pick a quarrel with him? He was doing his best to provoke her.

'However, any time you wish to quarrel with me in private I would be delighted to accommodate you.'

'If you had an ounce of sensibility you would realise that, under the circumstances, I want neither to speak to you nor to see you.'

'I take it you refer to the business with your brother. I cannot see what it has to do with you or...with you and me.'

She was floundering, badly out of her depth. Nothing in her limited experience with the opposite sex had ever prepared her to deal with a man such as Lord Stamford, a man with devastatingly dark expressive eyes, a man as handsome as the devil himself, a man who was flirting with her in a blatantly sensual fashion that caused her to feel vulnerable and utterly confused.

Desperate, she looked around for escape. With relief, she saw Lady Carlyn winding her way towards them. Her relief was short-lived when she noted the look of utter disbelief on her grandmother's face. What if Lord Stamford said something about this morning?

He must have read her mind for he said, 'There is no need to fear, my lady. I promise I will not tell your grandmother how you called on me in such a bold manner without so much as a maid to accompany you. As far as I am concerned, our first meeting has only now taken place. Of course, I shall not mention your fan. I will find a more private moment to return it to you.'

The wicked spark in his eye did nothing to reassure her, but it was too late to do a thing. Lady Carlyn had already made her way to them.

Lord Stamford's mouth curved in a disarming smile as he bowed over her plump hand. 'Lady Carlyn, I have just had the delightful opportunity of meeting your granddaughter. She is as lovely and charming as her grandmother.'

Lady Carlyn fluttered her lashes at him in a disgustingly flirtatious fashion. 'It's no use trying to turn my head at my age, young man. Rosalyn is much lovelier than I ever was. But how did you come to make her acquaintance? With a proper introduction, I trust?'

His eyes danced. 'Not at all. I was forced to introduce myself after she stumbled into my arms. Quite by accident, of course. But now that I have met her...I hope to secure your permission to call on her.'

A peculiar expression crossed her grandmother's face. 'You may, but I'll have you know I intend to keep a strict watch on her. She may be a widow, but she is not one of your flirts. I will not have you trifling with her.'

He turned his gaze on Rosalyn who felt as if she'd turned to stone. 'I shall behave with the utmost propriety.'

'That I shall have to see to believe.' Lady Carlyn stared at him for a moment. 'Very well, you may call on her.'

Rosalyn had to put a stop to this. 'It is quite doubtful that I would ever be at home to you, my lord.' And how could they discuss her as if she were in leading strings with no mind of her own? She did not know which one to strangle first.

'Nonsense. Of course you will, dear.' Lady Carlyn shot her a quelling glance.

A smile of pure devilment quirked his mouth. 'Unfortunately, I must depart now. I will see you soon, very soon, Lady Jeffreys.' Her name sounded like a caress on his lips.

He made an elaborate leg and strode off. Lady Carlyn watched his dark-haired figure weave its way through the crush.

With a bemused expression, she took Rosalyn's arm. 'My dear, I can scarcely believe this! Lord Stamford wishes to call on you. I cannot image why; he never pays the slightest heed to any respectable woman. Surely he cannot think that…no, of course not. Not with you dressed in that gown!'

'Isn't it fortunate that I wore it, then,' Rosalyn replied with a humourless smile. Her simply cut blue gown had been a source of contention between them, Lady Carlyn declaring it was fit only for a Methodist.

Rosalyn barely noticed as they made their goodbyes to Lady Winthrope, descended the crowded staircase, and waited a good twenty minutes for the carriage to be brought around. Her thoughts were totally occupied with the icy set-downs she planned to give Lord Stamford.

It wasn't until they had settled into the carriage and her grandmother spoke that Rosalyn started out of her reverie.

'My dear, what do you think of Lord Stamford? I hadn't even considered him. But now that I think of it—he would do quite nicely. No woman would ever be bored with him.'

'What are you talking about?'

'Lord Stamford. For a husband.'

'A husband?' Horrified, she stared at Lady Carlyn.

'I don't believe you've been attending at all. His aunt, Lady Spence, told me—in strict confidence, of course—that Eversleigh has been casting about for a wife for him. Why did I not think of this before? There is no reason why you should not be in the running. Now that you are finally in London, I shall call on Margaret and drop a hint in her ear.'

A most alarming headache was beginning in her right temple. 'Grandmama, please, no. I would rather be dead than ever, ever consider him for a husband.'

His most blatant efforts to flirt with her had failed dismally.

Michael received his overcoat and hat from the footman and headed down the steps into the cool spring night. He liked walking at night, despite the risk of footpads.

A smile curled his lips. It was wicked of him to tease Lady Jeffreys so much. Especially in front of Lady Carlyn. But the fire that sprang to her eyes and the all too-ready colour washing over her cheeks was too tempting to resist.

He had no idea why such a respectable widow should interest him. She was pretty but not beautiful. Her dress, even tonight, was unfashionably plain; no rows of lace and flowers adorned its hem, no low-cut bodice designed to reveal its wearer's charms. But it became her.

He usually found such ladies excessively dull. But not Lady Jeffreys. Behind the proper façade she tried to present, he sensed a warm, passionate woman. It would be a challenge for any man to storm those barriers.

Particularly as she detested him and made no pretense otherwise, not even in hopes he might relent and return her brother's estate. He admired her for that. At least she was honest in her dealings with him.

It would probably be too much to hope Miss Randall would harbour the same sentiments. No, from what he gathered of the young lady, she was very biddable and unlikely to disobey her family's wishes. A pity Lady Jeffreys was not his intended bride; he'd never get her to the altar unless she was drugged and bound.

Suddenly, Charles's words flashed through his mind. His head snapped up and he stopped dead in the quiet street, inspiration hitting him like a bolt of lightening. Why not? She was well bred, respectable, pretty, intelligent. And she disliked him thoroughly.

What more could he want in a prospective bride?

Having the proper, disapproving Lady Jeffreys in his power would be most agreeable. He'd wager any sum that by the end of their association, he could break down her resistance to him.

And he knew without doubt he could induce her to agree to his plan.

Chapter Three

Morning sunlight streamed through a crack in the heavy brocade curtains of Rosalyn's bedchamber. She fought to open her eyes, heavy with sleep, wanting nothing more than to snuggle back down into the cosiness of her bed.

It was these late nights. She was not used to staying up past midnight, let alone until two or three in the morning. She had never realized what energy a woman of sixty some years could possess. An evening at home was far too tame for Lady Carlyn; she must be out to a soirée or ball or to a concert every night. And she insisted Rosalyn accompany her.

Rosalyn struggled up as Mrs Harrod, her housekeeper, entered. She carried a tray with a pot of chocolate and a plate of toast.

'Anything else, my lady?' she asked as she set the tray in front of Rosalyn. She was plump and kindly and watched Rosalyn with a motherly eye. 'I thought you might like a tray today seeing how you did not come in until nearly three. Such a long night for you.'

Mrs Harrod bustled about, opened the curtains and

then departed. After pouring herself a cup of the steaming chocolate, Rosalyn sunk back on her pillows, wondering if there was any way she could escape tonight's ball. She had been to more of these affairs since arriving in London ten days ago than in the eight years since her own coming-out.

Her husband, John, had considered *ton* parties a frivolous waste of time, as did most of his scholarly colleagues. After the miserable, tongue-tied shyness of her one and only season, she had been grateful.

Sometimes she had longed for a little more gaiety. It seemed after the first year or so of their marriage, as he became more deeply immersed in completing the massive book he'd spent years working on, that anything which distracted him from his work was a waste of time.

Including her.

Tears pricked her eyes. She brushed them away with an angry hand. It was only that she had lost so many people she loved in the past five years, first John, then her mother a year later. Her father's spirit had been buried along with her mother, his body finally succumbing to a bout of influenza two years later. Now, she was losing James.

She had come to London, hoping to somehow bridge the gap between them. Since their mother's death, he'd walled off his emotions, rarely talking to her as he once had. Her father had been no help; lost in his own sorrow, he'd scarcely noticed James was growing more unmanageable, running around with some of the wildest young men in the neighbourhood. After her father died, he stayed away from Meryton for long periods of time, only once bringing a group of his new friends down for a week.

Rosalyn had been appalled. It took no more than a few hours in their company to discover he kept company with some of the most disreputable rakehells in London. She'd stayed out of their way, afraid to say anything to James for fear he'd shut her out even more. But he'd never asked them again.

She finally forced herself out of bed. Her abigail, Annie, helped her dress in a long-sleeved navy print cambric gown with a ruff around the throat, then dressed her hair in its usual knot.

Rosalyn had just reached the staircase when Mrs Harrod bustled up to her, her plump face shining with curious excitement.

'You have a visitor, my lady. I have shown him to the drawing room.'

'A visitor? Is it James?'

'No, not your brother.' Mrs Harrod clasped her hands. Her voice quivered with anticipation. 'It is the Marquis of Stamford, my lady. He wishes to see you.'

Rosalyn backed away from the staircase, her hand fluttering to her throat. What was he doing here so early? It was hardly the hour for morning callers. Did he think she was at his disposal at any time?

'Lord Stamford? He wishes to see me? Please inform him I am not at home.'

'But, my dear, he is very anxious to see you.'

'No, I certainly do not want to see him. It is much too early.'

Mrs Harrod pursed her lips in disapproval. When she saw Rosalyn did not plan to relent, she nodded and bustled away.

Irritated, Rosalyn turned back to her room. She supposed he'd finally decided to return her fan. A full
three days had passed since the rout. Well, he could
leave it with Mrs Harrod. She would hide out until he
left. She picked up a novel she was reading, but the
words jumbled into nonsense.

She jumped at the knock on her door. Mrs Harrod
poked her head around the edge, her face devoid of
expression.

'His lordship wishes me to inform you he will not
leave until you see him. He will wait for your con-
venience, even if it is past midnight.'

'That is most ridiculous.' But something about his
confident, overbearing manner made her think he was
perfectly capable of carrying out his threat, effectively
holding her prisoner in her room. She could hardly go
about her business while he cooled his heels in the
drawing room. What if someone called? Her grandmother, for instance. She closed her book and rose.

The strange sensation that her life was about to be
altered forever floated over her. But how silly—she
had never been prone to such fanciful notions.

With reluctant steps, she entered her drawing room.
The morning sun cast a friendly glow about the small
yellow room. Her unwanted visitor sat in one of the
armchairs near the fireplace, absorbed in a leather-
bound volume, his buckskin-clad legs stretched out before him. He didn't notice her presence for a few seconds and then he glanced up, closed the book and laid
it aside. He rose to his feet in a lazy movement.

He was dressed much as he had been the first time
she saw him, in riding coat and breeches, and top-
boots, his cravat tied carelessly about his neck. His

elegance looked out of place amidst the fading Oriental carpet and the comfortable but old-fashioned furnishings of the room.

His face was relaxed and his manner confident, as if there was no reason he was not perfectly welcome in her home.

'Lady Jeffreys, I did not expect to see you quite so soon. I was betting on some time in late afternoon.'

This threw her off completely. 'Indeed. I usually don't keep visitors waiting that long.'

'In my case, I was not sure. I am relieved, although my day is at your disposal. I decided to fetch a book from the library to occupy my time.'

'A book?'

'Does that astound you? I occasionally engage my mind in less dissipated pursuits, such as reading. I have even been known to pick up a volume of philosophy or history on occasion. But only when I have tired of sitting around a gaming table, stealing away estates or pursuing improper women.'

'Is there a purpose for your visit, my lord?' she asked with ice in her voice.

'Yes. To return your fan, of course. And to speak with you in private. I would not have called so early, except I did not want you to flee.' He held out her fan. She took it from him, careful to avoid any contact with his hand.

Her voice trembled for some odd reason. 'I see. I can't imagine what you would wish to speak to me about.'

'I wish to discuss your brother's gambling debt. I have a proposition to lay before you that I believe will benefit both of us. If you will sit, I will tell you.'

Even more confused, she quickly seated herself on one of the Queen Anne chairs. He settled back in the other, his eyes fixed on her face. The horrid premonition he was about to offer her another *carte blanche* caused her heart to beat uncomfortably fast. She folded her hands in her lap and waited.

'I do not think you will find my proposal too distasteful. I merely want you to become betrothed to me.'

Her heart stopped for a dizzying moment. 'What did you just say?'

'I would like you to become betrothed to me in exchange for returning your brother's estate to him.'

Her hand went to her throat. 'Betrothed to you! You must be mad! I would never consider such a thing!'

'Do you always answer your offers with such an excess of civility?' he inquired drily. 'Perhaps I didn't phrase it quite right. You don't need to marry me, merely become my fiancée for a short time. I am in need of a temporary fiancée.'

He sounded as if he were discussing the need for a new pair of boots.

'A temporary fiancée? Whatever for? I have never heard of anything so…so ridiculous!' She stood up and backed away from him towards the window, knotting her hands.

He rose and followed her. 'Not at all. My father has informed me it's high time I marry. He's already chosen the bride. I want to put a stop to his plans before I wake up one morning and find I'm expected to show up at the altar before noon. If I produce a fiancée of my own, I can hardly be expected to offer for the young lady he has in mind.'

'I…I should hope not.' He sounded so reasonable, Rosalyn had no doubt he was quite mad. 'But why me? I hardly think I would suit your purposes. We do not deal at all well together.'

A disarming smile settled over his features. 'You mean you wish me to perdition, my dear. There is no need to look so shocked, your face is far too honest. The strong aversion you've shown for my company suits me very well; I've no doubt you will be quite willing to cry off at the appropriate time. The bargain benefits both of us. You want your brother's estate back—it will be done. I avoid a marriage I don't want. And just consider, what could be more natural than for me to return Meryton to your brother as his future brother-in law? It will save a lot of explanation.'

'It is blackmail!'

'Hardly. Come now, Lady Jeffreys, what is so difficult? Is a few months in my company such a sacrifice for your brother? Just think how much you'll enjoy publicly jilting me in the end.'

Apparently the whole thing was nothing but a huge jest to him.

And how dare he be so confident that she would be delighted to play the role of his fiancée?

'A few months! I'd rather spend an eternity in hell than a day in your company.'

Her hand flew to her mouth, horrified at her rude words.

Something wholly unexpected crossed his face, but for such a fleeting moment, she was certain she had imagined it. Only slight amusement remained. 'Indeed? In that case, I shall leave you to plan your move from Meryton.'

He picked up his gloves and moved towards the door, then turned and bowed elaborately in her direction. 'However, I will leave my offer open for a day or so. In case you change your mind. Good day, my lady.'

'My lord, I am...' Before she could frame an apology, he quitted the room.

Mortified, she sank down on the sofa. Never had she said such an unkind thing to anyone. She tried to tell herself he richly deserved it, but she wasn't so certain. For one brief moment, he had looked as if her words had affected him. But no, that was impossible. Not the imperturbable Marquis of Stamford.

She put a hand to her head, which was beginning to ache in a familiar way. She could not possibly take him up on his preposterous suggestion, not even for James.

She stood up and took an agitated turn around the room.

But would a few months in his company really be such a high price to pay for Meryton? It was not as if he demanded she be his mistress. She had heard of men who were unscrupulous enough to ask for a woman's favours to pay off a debt. Not that she thought Lord Stamford was above that if it suited him. Most likely she was not to his taste, thank goodness. The thought of spending a night in his arms filled her with shivery panic.

She bit her lip, trying to think. What would they live on? John had left Rosalyn a small income and this house. The rest of his estate had been entailed to a nephew. Her competence could be stretched to accommodate two people in meagre comfort, but James would never accept that from her.

What would become of him?

She stared into the street with unseeing eyes. After all, how much time would she really be in his company? He was unlikely to spend much time dancing attendance on her. Such a flirt as Lord Stamford would undoubtedly find a woman more to his taste to occupy him.

She had no choice. She only prayed his offer was still open.

Michael entered Lady Burkham's crowded ball room at half past midnight. Almost immediately, Lady Burkham glided forward, and caught his arm. 'Why, Lord Stamford! We had given up all hope that you ever planned to show! I fear there has been more than one lady suffering from pangs of disappointment.'

'I doubt the affliction is permanent.'

Her smile faded a little at his cool tone. 'No, now that you are here. We are about to go down to supper. I hope you will partake of it.'

'Thank you. Your suppers are always superior.'

She smiled again and, after a few more remarks, departed. He watched the guests drift towards the doors, talking and laughing. The boredom he felt at these occasions assailed him. He regretted his impulse to come.

Except he'd felt equally bored at White's.

He finally admitted to himself he came in hopes of seeing Lady Jeffreys. Why, he had no idea. Until this morning, he had no doubt she would agree to his plan. But he had gravely miscalculated the depth of her dis-

like for him. Her words had stunned and then angered
him. He tried to tell himself it was only because her
refusal foiled his plans. He cared little what anyone
thought or said of him. Including Lady Jeffreys. But
a shaft of hurt he hadn't felt since his youth had shot
through him, piercing his careful armour of indifference.

This was ridiculous. He decided he would make his
excuses to his hostess and leave. Then he saw her.

She was going down to supper with Lady Carlyn.
Dressed in a dark blue gown that emphasised the gentle curve of her breasts, she looked delicately lovely.

He would stay after all.

He finally caught up to her at the supper laid out in
buffet style. He waited until she finished putting a lob-
ster patty on her plate before speaking.

'Lady Jeffreys.'

She whirled around and looked up at him as if he'd
sprung out of the wall. 'What are you doing here?'

He removed the plate from her hand since the food
appeared to be in danger of sliding to the table. 'I was
invited.'

'I only meant I had not yet seen you. Did…did you
get my note?'

'Note? No, although I have hardly been home. Does
this mean you wished to see me?'

'Yes.' Her face turned a delicate pink.

'Perhaps you could continue your conversation elsewhere?' Michael turned to find a stout gentlemen glaring at them.

Rosalyn quickly moved forward, Michael behind
her. 'Do you wish some strawberries? They look quite
good.'

She looked completely confused. 'Yes, I think so. This is for my grandmother.'

He put some strawberries on the plate. 'You are not eating?'

'I am not hungry.'

'So you hoped to see me? What has caused you to change your mind?' he asked softly.

She looked alarmed. 'Please, not here.'

'No.' He looked down the plate, now containing enough food to feed several elderly ladies. 'Is this enough for your grandmother?'

She eyed the plate doubtfully. 'I hope so.'

'Where is Lady Carlyn?'

He followed Rosalyn. Lady Carlyn sat at one of the long tables, between two older ladies. She beamed when she saw them. 'Lord Stamford! How kind of you to fetch my plate! And you have found my grand-daughter, I see. Perhaps you will join us.'

Lady Carlyn's voice carried. Rosalyn's face colour-ed as several heads craned their way.

'Actually, I had hoped to have a word with your granddaughter in private.' He smiled at Lady Carlyn.

'Why…why, I suppose so. Yes, but I trust you will be on your best behaviour!'

'Of course.' He took Rosalyn's arm, leading her from the room before Lady Carlyn could make any more pronouncements to the rest of the guests.

He led her to Lord Burkham's study. He closed the door and leaned against it, watching her face.

'What did your note say?'

'I wished to accept your offer,' she replied so softly he almost didn't hear her. She twisted her hands. Her face had all the appearance of one offering to take another's place on the gallows.

'So you decided a few months of misery in my company was worth the price of your brother's estate?'

Guilt washed across her delicate face. 'I didn't exactly mean that. I am sorry I said…'

He held up his hand. 'There is no need to apologise. Your sentiments towards me are quite clear. At least you are honest. Very well, my lady, your brother shall have his estate.'

She cast him a helpless, almost fearful look. 'What do you wish me to do now, my lord? Are we to announce our…our agreement right away?'

His mouth quirked slightly. 'I see no reason to delay the announcement of our…betrothal. As soon as our families are informed, I will put an announcement in the *Morning Post.*'

She looked almost horrified. 'Is that necessary?'

'It is quite necessary, my dear.'

'But what will everyone say? It seems so sudden. We hardly know each other.'

He shrugged. 'What does it matter? I am known for making up my mind quickly. Come, Rosalyn, the sooner this is settled, the sooner your brother will get his estate.'

The frightened look fled. 'I have not given you permission to use my given name, my lord.'

'You have my permission to use mine. You sound like my butler, not a woman who has accepted an offer of marriage.'

'But I have not accepted an offer of marriage. I am merely pretending to be betrothed to you. There is no need to be on such familiar terms when we are alone.'

He raised his brow. 'Pretending? No, you will be betrothed to me. You will be my fiancée and you will address me by my given name, Rosalyn.'

Her eyes flashed with anger. 'You will not dictate to me. I will call you whatever I please, my lord. I understood I was merely to become betrothed to you so you could avoid an arranged marriage. I do not think we need to expand our acquaintance beyond that. We shall do the bare minimum to establish that we are engaged and nothing more. You are free to go your own way.'

So she thought she could avoid him so easily, did she? He settled more firmly against the doorway and folded his arms. 'You're quite wrong,' he drawled. 'I have no intention of going my own way. If this is to succeed, I must play the role of the devoted fiancée. My Aunt Margaret, not to mention my father, has an uncanny ability to sniff out a scheme. In fact, I intend to make it clear I am in love with you. I shall accompany you everywhere and take as many opportunities as possible to be alone with you.'

'That is…is ridiculous. There is no need to go to such lengths.' She seemed at a loss for words, and then recovered herself. 'In fact, it is quite mad and I have no intention of going along with this. We can see each other once or twice a week and no more. I will not have you accompanying me about like some sort of…of lapdog.'

His eyes narrowed. 'Now you are attempting to dictate to me, my lady. I know you wish me to the devil, but we have a bargain. I will return your brother's estate and you will play the role of my fiancée. I expect some enthusiasm on your part for my company. Do you understand?'

She tilted her chin up, meeting his gaze. 'Quite, but I will not pretend to be in love with you. And I want you to understand I have no intention of engaging in idle flirtation with you when we are alone.'

They faced off for a moment like a pair of duellers, eyes locked. He finally shrugged. 'As you wish.'

He moved away from the door. 'I will escort you to the opera tomorrow. You will meet my sister and her husband. I will ask Lady Carlyn to accompany us.'

'Very well, my lord,' she replied.

'You had best begin to practise using my given name.'

'I have no idea what your given name is.'

'It is Michael.'

She said nothing, merely continuing to regard him as if she wished he would go away. He stepped towards her, causing her to put her hand to her necklace, and retreat a step back. He captured her slender hand and lifted it towards his lips, then pure devilment shot through him as he looked down at her. Without warning he pulled her to him, his lips brushing over hers.

She tasted cool and surprisingly sweet. He had a sudden urge to crush her to him. His hands dropped away.

'Until tomorrow, Rosalyn.' He dragged out her name with deliberate, intimate slowness. Her gaze flew to his face. There was no mistaking the apprehension in her eyes.

Chapter Four

Rosalyn stared down at the note, completely dismayed. Lady Carlyn, pleading a sudden headache, would not accompany them to the opera. Since her grandmother developed a headache only to avoid some commitment. Rosalyn suspected Lady Carlyn wanted her to be alone with Lord Stamford. She must have the only grandmother in London who actually encouraged her granddaughter to consort with rakes.

She crumpled the note, resisting the temptation to fling it across her bedchamber. Apprehension made her hand tremble. She had no desire to be alone with Lord Stamford, cooped up in his carriage across from him, forced to make conversation with a man she knew nothing about, a man whose power she was now in.

She was behaving in a ridiculous manner. She rose from her bed and peered distractedly into her looking glass, not really seeing her pale face. He had no power over her. She was hardly alone in the world; she had her family and her own small but adequate income. So there was nothing to fear. She would take part in

this absurd charade, Meryton would return to James,
and she would return to her safe, well-ordered world.

But nothing, she told herself, could dispel the sense
of dread she felt every time she thought of that fleeting
kiss. She must make it very clear that she had no intention of engaging in that sort of behaviour with him.

She turned from the mirror in an impatient movement and picked up her gloves and fan. A glance at
the small clock on her dressing table showed Lord
Stamford was already fifteen minutes late. The least
he could do was show up on time.

'My lady?'

Rosalyn started. Mrs Harrod peered around the edge
of the door. 'Lord Stamford is here. So very handsome
he is. All dressed in black. Like one of those heroes
in a novel.'

Even her housekeeper was charmed by the man.
Rosalyn picked up her velvet cloak from the bed. But
Mrs Harrod stepped in front of her before she could
leave. 'There's a bit of hair that's come out, my lady.'
With deft fingers, she pulled the offending lock back
into place. She stepped back and beamed, her kindly
face warm with admiration. 'There, my lady. You look
lovely. No wonder his lordship is so smitten.'

Rosalyn flushed, wishing her housekeeper did not
have such a romantic imagination.

She slowly descended the staircase, her heart beat-
ing much too fast. She entered her drawing room, the
lamps casting a cosy intimate glow about the room.

Lord Stamford stood in front of the fireplace, gazing
at the landscape over the mantelpiece, hands clasped
behind his back. He turned at her soft footsteps.

She caught her breath at his dashing appearance.

His black long-tailed coat, contrasted with the stark white of his ruffled shirt, became his dusky complexion and emphasised the lean, aristocratic planes of his face. A diamond glittered in the folds his white cravat. His hair, wavy from the misty rain, gleamed midnight in the lamplight. The black silk breeches and white stockings revealed a pair of muscular calves.

She tore her gaze away, praying he hadn't noticed her staring. She crossed the room towards him, arranging her features in what she hoped were cool, impersonal lines.

He took her hand and released it. His eyes searched her face. 'I hope I did not keep you waiting too long, Rosalyn.'

'Only a mere fifteen minutes, my lord.'

He grinned. ''Tis some improvement. Usually I am at least twenty minutes late. By the time our association is at an end, you may cure me of my propensity for lateness.'

He removed the cloak from her hands and stepped behind her. She felt the soft velvet slide around her shoulders. And then his hands stilled at the nape of her neck, making her feel as if every nerve had sprung to life.

'It is really your fault, you know,' he said.

'My fault?'

'You are not like most women. They are always at least ten minutes late to add to the stir their appearance will create. That is what I expected.'

'I don't like to waste time.' His touch distracted her so she hardly knew what she said.

He removed his hands and stepped around to observe her. His eyes took in her gown of black crêpe over a black sarcenet slip and the simple diamond necklace and matching ear drops.

'Certainly you didn't tonight.'

A blush crept over her face. Of course, he was a practised flirt who knew exactly how to gaze at a woman, making her feel as if she were especially lovely in his eyes. She dropped her eyes, attempting to get her thoughts in order. 'My grandmother will not accompany us, my lord. She has the headache.'

'She has already informed me.' He continued to watch her with a penetrating look that made her uncomfortable.

'Perhaps we should depart, my lord.' She turned away and picked up her reticule.

'Michael,' he said.

'I beg your pardon?'

'Address me by my given name, Rosalyn.'

'Until we announce our…agreement, I do not think it is necessary to be on such familiar terms.'

'I think it is. My name is not that difficult. I want to hear you say it.'

He moved in front of her. She recognised that particular half-smile and knew they could be here all night if she didn't comply with his request.

'Very well…Michael.' Her voice was barely above a whisper.

He leaned towards her, his fingertips lightly brushing her cheek. 'That is a good beginning. My name sounds very nice on your lips.'

She could think of nothing to say as she sat across from him on the comfortable cushions of the coach. Even the weather seemed too difficult to discuss.

There was nothing but the sound of the horses' hooves on the street and the soft patter of rain on the coach. She hardly knew where to look and mostly stared down at her hands. Finally she glanced up at Lord Stamford, lounging in his corner, and found his unfathomable eyes fixed on her face.

'Must you stare at me in such a way?'

'What way is that?'

'As if you mean to memorise my features. Or as if I am some strange creature! It is most unnerving and quite rude.'

'My apologies, but you have the most expressive features. I find it fascinating to watch your emotions play across your face.'

'I cannot imagine why you would find that so interesting.' She'd always disliked her inability to hide her feelings. It made her feel vulnerable and, at times, awkward. And now with Lord Stamford, she wanted more than anything to present a cool, remote exterior. Instead, he was telling her she had a face that displayed her every emotion.

'Can't you? Perhaps it is because I've known too many women who hide their every thought and feeling under a carefully cultivated veneer.'

'Sometimes I think that would be an advantage.'

'It's not. I prefer honesty.'

She looked away from him, even more disconcerted.

The coach finally halted, and she saw they were near the Opera House. Several carriages waited in line before them. She watched a gentleman followed by an elegantly dressed lady glittering with jewels, and then a younger lady in the dress of a debutante, descend from the coach. The man was dressed much as Lord Stamford in the dark coat and breeches required for admittance to the opera. The young lady stared up at the impressive rectangular building with its façade of columns marching across the row and seemed to bounce in excitement.

It brought to mind her season when she first saw the elegant King's Theatre. She had been so nervous, in her white muslin gown and pearls, as she accompanied Lady Carlyn up the steps and passed through the portico with all the *haute ton* milling about. She could barely speak when she was introduced to some of Lady Carlyn's elegant acquaintances. But she had merely been one among a throng of young girls presented that season and hardly dazzled anyone. No one stared much at her arrival or fixed a quizzing glass on their box. It had been both a relief and a disappointment.

Stamford lightly touched her arm, causing her to jump. 'Rosalyn, we are here. We cannot spend the evening in the carriage.'

She abruptly returned to Stamford's coach and saw the footman had flung open the door. Stamford alighted in one swift, graceful movement and held out his hand to her.

She accepted his assistance, but stumbled a little, so he was forced to steady her. She started away from the unnerving contact and then dropped her reticule at his feet.

He retrieved the bag, handing it to her with his characteristic half-smile. 'Have you always had the unfortunate habit of dropping your reticule?'

'Only since I've met you.' Thank goodness for the

dark, so he couldn't see the dark blush that she knew stained her face and neck.

'That is not the usual effect I have on women.'

She coloured even more, and vowed to avoid any further contact with him. But he lightly caught her arm before they entered the portico, turning her to face him. The half-shadows kept her from clearly seeing his expression.

'Before we go in, there is something I must make clear to you,' he began.

'Yes?'

'I think you fear that I intend to offer you another *carte blanche* as part of our bargain. In light of my conduct at our first meeting, I cannot blame you, but rest assured, I have no intention of doing so. I do not force women to my bed.'

'Of…of course not,' she stammered.

He drew her arm through his as they passed through the doors into the crowded entrance hall.

If she had received little attention during her season, it was made up tenfold tonight. Heads swivelled as they passed. Stamford paid no heed, merely nodding to acquaintances without pausing, his hand resting possessively on her arm as he guided her through the elegantly dressed crowd. Heat flooded her cheeks but she managed to keep her head high.

As they reached the circular staircase, a woman stepped away from a small group and clutched Stamford's arm, forcing him to halt.

'Dear Stamford! How surprising to see you! You have been so scarce I thought you'd left town. And how remiss of you to not have yet called on me.'

She was tall and well built with a fascinating sultry

face. Her low-cut emerald gown revealed a creamy expanse of flesh. Jade-green eyes flickered over Rosalyn, then dismissed her.

'I have been busy,' Stamford replied shortly, his face haughty. He began to move away, but she caught his arm.

'Come riding with me tomorrow, then. I have not seen you for an age.'

'I cannot. Elinor, if you will excuse me.'

'You're always so difficult. At least introduce me to your companion.' Her smile held a touch of malice.

Stamford looked discomfited. 'Lady Jeffreys, may I present Lady Marchant?'

Lady Marchant ran her eyes up and down Rosalyn as if she were summing up an enemy before battle. 'How nice to meet you,' she finally replied, an insincere smile pasted on her lips.

Stamford nearly wrenched Rosalyn away. 'We must go.'

Rosalyn eyed his cool face with fascination. She had never seen him at such disadvantage. With sudden intuition, she knew the voluptuous Lady Marchant was or had been his mistress. How very awkward to be forced to introduce one's mistress to the lady one was to be betrothed to. And how very fortunate Rosalyn was not really his fiancée.

As if sensing her gaze, he turned his head and look down at her with unsmiling eyes. 'Do you find fault with my appearance? Is that why you are staring?'

'Not at all. I was thinking how nice it was to meet Lady Marchant. She is very lovely. Is she a particular friend of yours?'

His eyes narrowed. She met his suspicious gaze with innocent eyes. 'No,' he replied shortly.

'Do you often ride with her in the park?'

This time he openly glared. 'That is none of your business. That is—' He stopped and clamped his lips in a tight line. 'I assure you I have nothing to do with Lady Marchant. She is an acquaintance, that is all. Does that satisfy your curiosity?'

She averted her head to hide the smile tugging at her lips. How gratifying to know it was possible to provoke Lord Stamford.

The curtain had already lifted on the singers by the time they took their seats. To her surprise, there was no one else in the box.

He must have noted her puzzlement for he leaned towards her, his breath fanning her cheek. 'We will meet my sister and her husband later. I did not wish to entirely overwhelm you.'

He settled back in the box; his eyes fixed on the stage. She stared around the theatre; it looked much as she remembered from her season; the tiers of boxes painted cerulean blue and gold filled to capacity with glittering ladies and handsomely dressed gentlemen, the fops strolling in the pit; the stares, the whispers behind fans as subjects for scandal-broth were spotted.

Only this time many of the glances were directed at their box. She felt as self-conscious as if they were sitting on the stage themselves.

She hoped James wasn't here. She knew she would have to break the news of her agreement—no, betrothal to Stamford, soon. She would rather do it in person than have the news leak to him. She looked around the theatre again and then her gaze fell on

Edmund Fairchilde sitting a few boxes away. To her great consternation, he had a quizzing glass fixed on her face. She quickly turned away, only to find Stamford observing her.

'Is there something wrong?'

'No, I…I wished to see if my brother was here.'

'The thought seems to fill you with dismay,' he remarked.

Why could he read her so easily? 'I didn't tell him I was coming with you.'

His mouth quirked. 'I see. That is quite cowardly of you.'

She twisted her hands in her lap. 'I am afraid I am something of a coward.'

'I wouldn't say that. Otherwise, you would not be here with me.'

His words were completely unexpected. She glanced at him, taken aback, hardly knowing what to say. She fixed her eyes on the stage.

Concentrating on the performance proved impossible. She was too aware of the man beside her and of how alone they were, despite the filled boxes. More than once his arm brushed hers, causing her to flinch. She was grateful when the curtain finally fell and the last of the opera dancers flounced off stage for the interval.

'Did you enjoy the performance at all?' Stamford asked.

'Oh…of course. It was very nice,' she murmured, hardly recalling what took place.

'I am not certain you did. You seemed rather distracted.'

'I had forgotten how inquisitive people could be in London.'

'I take it you don't like being the focus of so much curiosity and speculation?'

'No, not at all. Do you?'

His mouth twisted in a sardonic half-smile. 'I am quite used to it, so I pay no heed. Don't trouble yourself about it. They will soon find a more scandalous *on dit* to occupy them.' He held out his hand, assisting her to her feet. 'But for now, my dear lady, I am afraid you must put up with more turned heads. I am going to introduce you to my sister and her husband.'

He led her past the curious stares and whispers down to the saloon, already crowded and noisy with patrons wishing to procure refreshments. They approached a small group standing in one corner.

'Michael!' A stocky fair-haired gentleman turned around and grinned. 'Here so soon? Didn't expect you to show before the last act!'

One of the two ladies standing next to the gentleman laughed. 'That's too kind! I would have said the—' She broke off, her eyes wide with astonishment as she caught sight of Rosalyn.

'I had no idea you were bringing someone,' the lady said, her voice cool. Her haughty gaze brushed over Rosalyn's face. Dark-haired with an olive complexion, her relation to Stamford was unmistakable—she could only be his sister, Lady Hartman.

The other three, the stocky gentleman, the red-haired lady standing next to him and a taller man, observed her with polite curiosity.

Stamford took Rosalyn's hand, pulling her to his side. 'May I present Lady Jeffreys? Lord and Lady

Hartman, my cousin Charles Portland, and his fiancée, Elizabeth Markham.' He pulled her even more close and said blandly, 'You must congratulate us. Lady Jeffreys has done me the honour of accepting my hand in marriage.'

The effect could not have been more startling if he had pulled a pistol on them. They froze and stared in stunned silence until Lady Hartman spoke.

'You cannot be serious. Is this one of your jests?'

'I am quite serious. She finally made up her mind to accept my offer yesterday.'

'Good God!' exclaimed Mr Portland faintly. He exchanged a glance with Miss Markham and then turned a fascinated eye on his cousin.

'But does Papa know this? Michael, he—' began Lady Hartman.

'This is hardly the time to discuss the matter,' Stamford replied coolly. His hand closed more tightly about Rosalyn's, who was experiencing the nightmarish sensation of having been plopped down in the middle of a farce without having read the script.

Then Lord Hartman stepped forward and took her hand. Grey eyes twinkled in a pleasant countenance. 'Let me be the first to congratulate you. We are, of course, surprised, although I have no idea why. We always suspected Michael would waste no time once he met the right lady.' His smile was reassuring. 'I had the pleasure of meeting you once a long time ago when I attended a lecture of Sir John's. I was acquainted with him, and you were there. I was sorry to hear of his death; he was a good man and a talented scholar. But I am delighted you have found happiness again.'

'Thank you,' Rosalyn replied, touched by his kind words for John and grateful for his courtesy towards her. She smiled a little shyly. 'I'm sorry I do not recall meeting you, my lord.'

'No matter. I am glad to renew our acquaintance.' He turned to his wife. 'My dear?'

Lady Hartman's bright, inquisitive gaze never wavered from Rosalyn's face. Slender and vivacious with dark hair tumbling about in charming disarray, she resembled a pixie. A smile of pure mischief spread over her countenance. 'What delightful and unexpected news. But you must tell me, wherever did you meet my brother?'

'At…' began Rosalyn.

'At Lady Winthrope's rout,' Stamford replied firmly.

'But that was only two days ago! I see, Michael, you have tumbled into love at last! Who would have thought this would happen! Lady Jeffreys, you must tell me all about yourself. Where are you from?'

'Caro, it is not necessary to interrogate Lady Jeffreys.' His face took on the haughty look Rosalyn was beginning to recognise as irritation.

His sister blithely ignored his black look. 'Oh, but it is.' She turned back to Rosalyn with an innocent smile. 'At least tell me how my brother persuaded you to marry him. I can't imagine how any woman in her right mind would accept his offer. Did he bribe you?'

Mr Portland, who had been silent, emitted a strangled cough.

'My dear, Lady Jeffreys is not used to your ragmannered ways,' said Lord Hartman.

'Well, did he?' persisted Lady Hartman.

It was all Rosalyn could do to maintain her countenance. 'Not quite,' she managed.

Lady Hartman crowed. 'Now I am even more curious. We must have a coze when my brother is not present.'

'Very pleased for you, Michael. Never thought you could pull it off,' Mr Portland said.

'And I am also very pleased for you,' Miss Markham said.

Mr Portland grasped Rosalyn's hand and grinned. 'Best wishes to you, my lady. Welcome to the family. We're all quite insane, you know. Just keep that in mind and don't let us eat you.'

'Thank you,' said Rosalyn, dazed.

'Charles, what a thing to say!' scolded Miss Markham.

Her fiancé smiled lazily. 'You've often said the same thing; we're all quite mad.'

'Now that you've all managed to properly scare her with such an encouraging welcome, I'd best take her back to our box,' Stamford said coolly.

He first procured Rosalyn a glass of lemonade she did not want, then fixed her with such a fierce stare she felt obligated to force it down her throat. Her temper was beginning to flare over his high-handedness and utter lack of sensibility for all concerned.

Michael was not at all surprised to have Rosalyn round on him once they reached their box. Her hazel eyes flashed fire. She didn't look a bit like the compliant fiancée he'd envisioned. In fact, he'd seen the same expression in his aunt's eyes more than once.

'How could you spring this on them?'

He fixed her with his most bland look. 'What do you mean?'

'You know what I mean. They were so shocked. That was hardly kind of you. You might have at least prepared them in some way.'

'I suppose you wanted me to drop sly hints and be seen in your company an appropriate amount of time before declaring my intentions, is that it?'

She snapped her fan shut. 'What is wrong with that? It would have been the most courteous thing to do.'

He leaned back in his seat and said in his most annoying drawl, 'I assure you, my family would be more surprised if I were to be courteous. This is more what they expect out of me.'

'Indeed. I feel quite sorry for them. And for your future wife if she has to put up with this!'

He was beginning to enjoy himself. 'I will make it worth her while in—other ways.'

He was delighted to see a dark blush stain her cheeks, but she rallied. 'I am certain nothing would be worth it.'

'Now that we're engaged, it would be quite proper of me to demonstrate and let you make up your mind,' he suggested wickedly.

She looked shocked. He must learn to curb his tongue when with her. She was not one of his flirts who would parry his double-edged remarks with an even more suggestive one.

'Besides, I want to squelch any rumours.'

'What rumours?' she asked.

'Rumours about our association.' The puzzlement on her expressive face brought him up short. He found himself unable to tell her there were already bets on the book on how long it would take him to make her his next mistress. She would be appalled.

'I wanted to make certain no one would claim your hand and your affections before we announce our, er...agreement.'

'Since I plan never to remarry there was very little danger that would overset your plans.'

'Why don't you wish to remarry? You are a very lovely woman. I'm surprised you don't have suitors falling over themselves,' he said carelessly.

'I hardly consider that a compliment. Perhaps your only criterion for judging a woman's worth is her beauty or lack of it, but I hope most men don't use that in looking for a wife.'

'You are right, of course, there are more important qualities in a woman than beauty. I do beg your pardon. But tell me, do you consider a man's appearance important?'

'Yes, I generally find the degree of handsome looks a man possesses also determines his degree of conceit.'

He grinned. '*Touché,* my lady. Are you perhaps referring to myself?'

'I didn't exactly say that.'

'No, not exactly. But at least you consider me somewhat handsome. How much conceit do you think I possess?'

She glared at him and turned away.

He eyed his betrothed's profile as she sat concentrating very hard on the performance, ignoring him. Somehow he had entertained the erroneous notion Lady Jeffreys would prove to be quite compliant once he bent her to his will. She appeared so quiet and reserved, which in his experience translated into malleable. He could see now she intended to cross swords with him at every opportunity. A grin creased his face. Suddenly, a betrothal seemed a much more interesting state of affairs than he'd ever imagined.

Chapter Five

Watkins stepped aside as Lady Spence stormed into his master's study. She marched over to the desk where Michael sat writing, a militant expression on her face. Michael put down his pen and looked up, then rose to his feet.

A slight smile crossed his face. 'I somehow thought I would see you today.'

'You might,' she said briskly, seating herself on the other side of the desk. She pulled off her gloves and eyed her nephew coldly. 'I saw Caroline earlier today.'

'Did you?'

'Michael! She said you presented a…a woman to them at the opera last night whom you claimed was your fiancée. I simply cannot believe this! It cannot be true.'

'It is quite true. Only I did not claim she *was* my fiancée, she *is* my fiancée.'

'Impossible!'

'Not at all. Why is everyone so surprised? You have been hounding me to the altar for the past six years. It is my duty to marry eventually.'

'Don't be dense. You know perfectly well what I mean,' snapped Lady Spence. 'The negotiations for your marriage to Miss Randall have already been started.'

'What sort of negotiations?' Michael inquired, his voice cool. He came around to the side of the desk and lounged against it. 'You're not trying to tell me a marriage has already been arranged without my consent to a woman I've never met? I've told you and my father I would not agree to this scheme. I've no desire to marry a girl fresh from the schoolroom merely because my father and that old martinet Sheringwood have come up with some idiotic notion there needs to be an alliance between the two families. I will chose my own wife.'

Lady Spence snorted. 'You are quite mistaken if you think your father will consent to this. I am almost afraid to ask who this woman might be. Caroline wouldn't tell me; she seemed to find the whole matter highly entertaining. I only pray it is not Elinor Marchant.'

'Put your fears to rest. I don't think you'll find her at all disagreeable. She is Rosalyn, Lady Jeffreys. I believe you are acquainted with her grandmother, Lady Carlyn.'

Lady Spence jerked her head up, her face losing its cool composure. 'Rosalyn Jeffreys? Oh, no! Michael, she could not have possibly consented to marry you. She is much too respectable!'

Stamford sat on one edge of the desk and fingered the letter opener. A sardonic smile crossed his face. 'My family is so highly complimentary. Is it so difficult to believe a respectable lady might possibly wish to marry me? Or am I too far beyond the pale? I am surprised you wish to throw the innocent Miss Randall into my clutches.'

'It is not that, Michael. I have always thought that if you met the right woman…' She stopped, her eyes full of concern. 'Never mind. But where did you meet her? Lady Carlyn constantly complains she'll never come to London.'

'She is here now. I met her at the Winthropes' rout. I was instantly charmed. Have you made her acquaintance?'

'A long time ago, during her first season. Lady Carlyn sponsored her. She was such a quiet little thing, very pretty with large eyes and dark hair, but so shy—she had nothing to say. Lady Carlyn despaired of ever finding a match for her. But, Michael, unless she has changed, she is hardly in your style! As I remember she is very proper and reserved. I cannot believe you would even notice her.'

'But I did. I discovered those were the qualities I wanted in a wife. After our first meeting, I decided I would ask her for her hand.'

Lady Spence looked at her nephew with exasperation. 'And she accepted. Oh, dear! I have long prayed you would meet a woman that would show you at least a measure of resistance. I rather pity Lady Jeffreys if she has fallen in love with you.' She rose to her feet, clearly agitated. 'Michael, this is a very difficult situation. You have offered marriage to Lady Jeffreys so you cannot with honour back away from it. But there is Miss Randall to consider. Certain promises have been made to her also.'

'But I did not make them. I have never met Miss

Randall. I cannot conceive why she would be particularly eager to marry a man she has not met. Has she ever given you any indication she wishes to marry me?'

'No, she has not,' Lady Spence said slowly. She thought for a minute. 'I think she wishes to do her duty, but I've never had any strong feeling that she considered the marriage as settled. I believe she was told the marriage would take place after you had met and decided there was some compatibility. It is not likely that it will be Miss Randall who will feel slighted but rather Lord Sheringwood and Eversleigh. Your father will kick up quite a dust over this, Michael.'

'He'll settle down. He'll be so pleased that I have at last found a suitable bride he'll forget he didn't choose her himself. And I am certain he will consider Lady Jeffreys quite suitable. She is well-bred; her manners are pleasing; she is intelligent. Just imagine how relieved he'll be that I didn't bring home one of my dashing widows.'

'I don't think he'll be that pleased to have his plans overset.' Lady Spence stared at him with a frown. 'You're up to something, aren't you, Michael? How very convenient for you to find a bride in the nick of time. Are you in love with Lady Jeffreys?'

Michael shrugged and said lightly, 'I have been in love a hundred times. But I am very fond of Lady Jeffreys. She is pretty and charming and intelligent, and I will endeavour to be a good husband.'

Lady Spence rolled her eyes upwards. 'God help her. You'll lead her a merry dance. Well, what will you say to your father?'

'I was hoping you would help out in that regard. He'll listen to you,' said Michael. His mouth curved in an engaging smile.

'I shall have to meet Lady Jeffreys again before I attempt to do any such thing. I still can't believe you actually plan to marry someone decent. I would have been less surprised if you had announced you wanted to marry Lady Marchant or one of the other ill-bred creatures you've associated with. Sometimes I have felt you deliberately go out of your way to find the most annoying and vulgar sorts merely to irritate your father and the rest of the family as well.'

Michael grinned. 'Caroline has frequently accused me of the very same thing.'

'You're a rogue, Michael.' She sighed. 'And far too charming for your own good. I will call on Lady Jeffreys and decide if I wish to plead your cause.'

'Don't scare her too much. Caroline did a pretty good job of it last night, and Charles informed her she was marrying into a family of lunatics.'

Lady Spence pulled on her gloves and tied the ribbons of her bonnet. 'She is. There is no need to hide the truth from her. Perhaps she will come to her senses in time. However, I promise not to intimidate her.'

'Thank you.'

Michael accompanied her to her waiting carriage and handed her in.

Lady Spence started towards home and then changed her mind. She tapped the roof of her carriage with her parasol and instructed the coachman to drive to Grosvenor Street. She would call on Lady Carlyn. The whole affair was highly suspicious. She had fully expected Michael to find a way to defeat his father's plan, for he was as stubborn and high-handed as the Duke in getting his own way. He had successfully blocked the Duke's move this time, but who would win the game was still up in the air.

Rosalyn had barely removed her pelisse when Mrs Harrod bustled into her bedchamber to inform her that Lady Spence had come to call. 'She is such an elegant woman, my lady. Such an honour to have her come, for she moves in the highest circles. You shall want to change your dress.'

Rosalyn looked down. Mud had spattered across the bottom of her cream gown. In the past few days she had begun walking in Green Park with Annie, her abigail, wanting to escape from the confusion her life had suddenly become. The park with its dairymaids and cows reminded her a little of the country.

Usually, her walks were peaceful. But not today. She had been pestered by a fop in a revoltingly green frock coat over a butter-coloured waistcoat who persisted in speaking to her in a bold manner. Her most icy demeanour hadn't fazed him. He flustered her so much she stepped in a mud puddle, soaking her kid half-boots and splashing mud on her gown.

And now Lady Spence, Lord Stamford's formidable aunt, the aunt with the uncanny perception, sat below. She vaguely recalled meeting Lady Spence years ago, but could remember little about her. She pushed back her hair, trying to think. She wished she could send Lady Spence away and crawl under the covers pleading a headache, but she knew that would hardly do. She sighed. 'Yes, I shall change. Please inform Lady Spence I will be with her shortly.'

* * *

Rosalyn finally entered the drawing room, her hands clammy. She saw an elegant, aristocratic lady with a fine-boned face and observant blue eyes, immaculately dressed in a dark green spencer over a dress of pomona green. Her cool appearance as well as the speculative look in her eyes would have been quite intimidating, except for the warmth of her clasp as she took Rosalyn's hand and the kindness that lit her face.

'Thank you for receiving me on such short notice, Lady Jeffreys, but I had to come. I saw my nephew this morning and he told me the delightful and most unexpected news. Congratulations, my dear. We are so very pleased that Michael will be wed at last.'

Rosalyn was momentarily stunned. 'Thank you,' she said, feeling the colour mount her cheeks. 'Won't you please be seated, my lady?'

Lady Spence sat down on the small sofa near the fireplace. She patted the spot beside her. 'Come and sit by me, my dear. I want to hear all about this. I could get very little out of my nephew, which is so like him.'

With some trepidation, Rosalyn sat down beside Lady Spence, catching a whiff of her delicate perfume. She waited.

Lady Spence turned to her. 'So you met Michael at the Winthropes' rout? He said he was instantly charmed by you.'

'Did he?' Rosalyn asked faintly.

'Yes, he was determined to marry you after the first meeting. I never thought he could be so romantic.'

She didn't seem to notice the dismay Rosalyn could not quite keep from her face. She continued blithely on. 'I imagine he quite overwhelmed you. He is that way when he wants something. Your grandmother said you did not particularly care for Michael at the outset.'

'You have seen my grandmother?'

'Yes, before I came here. She will come to call on you later today to congratulate you. She had not been certain last night that you would accept him.'

The world was beginning to spin. 'Last night? I do not understand.'

Lady Spence's smile was bland. 'Did Michael not tell you he called on your grandmother yesterday to assure her his intentions were honourable?'

'No, he…he never said a thing.'

'That is not surprising. So Michael overcame your resistance. Tell me, Lady Jeffreys, what do you think of my nephew now?'

'I beg your pardon?'

Lady Spence's lips curved in a slight smile. 'Lord Stamford, my nephew. What do you think of him?'

Rosalyn was momentarily confused. What did she think of Lord Stamford? What she thought would hardly be polite to say to his aunt. She decided on a neutral tact. 'He is very amiable,' she replied cautiously.

This time it was Lady Spence who looked startled. 'Amiable?' she repeated. She looked at Rosalyn with frank interest.

Rosalyn realized she had blundered. She should have come up with a more enthusiastic answer.

To her relief, Lady Spence suddenly smiled. 'Forgive me for sounding so surprised, but I don't believe I have ever heard Michael described as amiable. Certainly by many other terms, including exasperating and overbearing, if you talk to his sisters, but never merely amiable! Do you find him at all charming?'

'He can be when it pleases him,' Rosalyn replied truthfully.

Lady Spence didn't seem displeased with her answer. 'That is very good. He is the sort of man that one should never be too charmed by. Are you in love with him?'

Rosalyn's mouth fell open. Certainly his family asked the most amazing questions. 'I…what?'

Lady Spence looked amused. 'I can see you are not. Thank goodness, I was quite worried about that. If you were in love with him, I would caution you against marrying him.'

Rosalyn could only stare. She felt as if she'd wandered into a family of Bedlamites.

Lady Spence apparently did notice her dazed look. 'Eversleigh will be quite pleased with you once he accepts Michael has defied his wishes. He doesn't like to be crossed, but no matter. He'll come around. You probably know he was trying to arrange a match for my nephew. Michael was quite against it. How fortunate the match didn't take place before he met you. I think you will be quite good for Michael.'

'I…I hope so,' Rosalyn said uncertainly. The shrewdness in Lady Spence's eyes rendered her uneasy. She had the odd feeling Lord Stamford's aunt knew something was amiss, but for reasons of her own, chose not to say anything. She only hoped she would never meet the Duke. She fumbled about in her mind for something else to say.

'We will need to discuss the wedding.'

'Wedding?'

'It should take place as soon as possible. Your grandmother and I thought perhaps in six weeks, at the end of June. That should give us enough time to make the necessary arrangements.'

'In six weeks?' Rosalyn exclaimed in panic. She had never dreamed anyone would actually wish to discuss a date for the non-existent wedding. 'That seems so...so soon.'

Lady Spence raised delicate brows. 'So soon? We have been waiting for my nephew's wedding date for the past decade. And Michael was in such a hurry to persuade you to marry him, that I don't think he'll wish to wait very long. In fact, I am certain he will not.'

'I...' Rosalyn was at a loss for words. She racked her brain for some plausible reason they could not marry so quickly. And if her grandmother was involved... Rosalyn shuddered inwardly. They'd be at the altar before they could turn around.

'I had really hoped for an autumn wedding,' she found herself saying. 'I love the autumn, the leaves are so pretty and it is my favourite time of the year. And Lord...Michael and I would like to become better acquainted.'

'I see.' Lady Spence regarded her curiously. 'I quite understand. An autumn wedding will be ideal if that is what you wish.'

'Oh, yes!'

'We will give a small dinner for you next week to celebrate your betrothal,' Lady Spence said.

'Surely a dinner is not necessary.'

'Of course it is. We must celebrate your engagement

and formally introduce you to society as the next Marchioness of Stamford.'

'But, I don't think…'

Lady Spence rose. 'My dear, I am certain this is all quite overwhelming for you. Now, I will leave so you may rest. You will attend the Fawnworths' ball tonight, I understand. I shall look forward to seeing you there.'

She embraced Rosalyn and then left, leaving Rosalyn staring after her in a daze.

Mrs Harrod's voice jerked her out of her reflections. 'My lady, you've another visitor.'

'I shall announce myself.' Lady Carlyn pushed past Mrs Harrod into the room. 'Oh, my love! I knew how it would be! There was something in his manner… We haven't a moment to waste! This time you will have a proper wedding!'

Rosalyn sunk back on the sofa. This charade of a betrothal was going to be much more complicated than she'd ever imagined.

Rosalyn stood in one corner of Lady Fawnworth's ballroom, which had been decorated as a Greek temple with vines running up false pillars, statues of nymphs and goddesses tucked in corners. The lively strains of a country dance filled the room as the dancers galloped through the steps.

Lady Carlyn chattered with an acquaintance, occasionally flinging a delighted smile in Rosalyn's direction. Rosalyn suspected she could scarcely contain the news of Rosalyn's betrothal. She had declared it was certain to be the coup of the Season.

Rosalyn was already experiencing regrets. Not only

must she deal with Lord Stamford but now with her grandmother. She sighed and shifted positions. At least one problem had not yet arrived.

Her eyes strayed towards the doorway as the music ended. She stiffened, all of her senses springing to life. Lord Stamford entered the ballroom with his usual air of nonchalant elegance. As he strolled into the room, she noticed several feminine heads turning in his direction. He paid little attention, his eyes roving over the room. Undoubtedly looking for her. Rosalyn fled.

She found an unoccupied spot behind a pillar, near one wall of the ballroom. Rational thought returned. Whatever was she doing? She had to face him some time this evening. It was only that she'd had a sudden vision of her grandmother making some embarrassing remark designed to hint to anyone within hearing that a special announcement was to be expected soon.

'Hiding, my sweet?'

She gasped and spun around. Lord Stamford stood next to her, a slight half-smile lifting his lips.

'Oh! I did not hear you!'

'Is there a particular reason you are standing behind this pillar? Your grandmother said you suddenly disappeared. If I wasn't so certain of your delight in seeing me, I would almost think you were avoiding me.'

He leaned one shoulder against the wall and crossed his arms. The movement emphasised the muscles beneath his black evening coat. Perhaps she should have chosen a spot where she wouldn't feel so cornered. 'I always find balls so stifling. I suddenly needed some fresh air.'

'You would do better if you stood near a window.

Come, I want to dance with you.' He held out his hand.

She stared at his hand as if it were a hot coal. 'Thank you, but I really don't care to dance tonight.'

'And why is that?'

'I am rather tired, that is all.' His brows shot up. She stumbled on, 'That is, I haven't danced much, and I…I will probably step on your feet.'

'I doubt that.' He moved away from the wall towards her, causing her to back up a few steps. 'My dear Rosalyn, perhaps I did not make this clear to you. I expect you to behave like a proper fiancée in public. Not only will you dance with me, I expect you to make it clear you find the experience enjoyable.'

His dictatorial tone set her back up. 'And how am I suppose to do that?'

'You will smile at me, and attempt some sort of conversation. I do not want you to give my family any reason to suspect why you accepted my offer.'

'So you wish me to lead them to believe I accepted you for your wealth and title?'

He gave her a startled glance and then suddenly grinned. 'So you do have claws, my dear.' His voice dropped to an intimate level. 'I was rather hoping you would lead them to believe you fell head over ears for me the first time we met. That is the impression I hope to create.'

Rosalyn felt colour rise up her face. 'I really wish you would not. It will only make everything more complicated.'

'Why?'

'Won't it be more difficult to explain why we do

not suit in the end if you are pretending to be in…that is, hold a fondness for me?'

He snorted. 'Hold a fondness for you? You do have an interesting way of putting things. Don't you mean if I am in love with you?'

'I really don't know what I mean! Perhaps we should dance.' She looked around to find several people staring at them, including a dandy who had levelled his quizzing glass on her face.

'An excellent idea.' He took her arm, leading her around the side of the pillar. The musicians were striking up the notes of a waltz.

'Oh, dear,' Rosalyn said faintly. Not a waltz. The dance had only gained formal acceptance last year and she had never danced it in public.

'Now what is wrong?' Lord Stamford asked, as he led her to the ballroom floor.

'I can't waltz with you. Not here.'

'Do you wish to waltz with me in private then? I must admit that might be more interesting.'

'That is not what I meant! I have never danced the waltz in a ballroom before. In front of people!'

His mouth quirked as he looked down at her. 'I have no doubt you'll manage quite well.' He placed one hand lightly above her waist and drew her into position, then began to move in time to the music.

He was a graceful dancer and, after treading on his foot once, Rosalyn managed to follow him.

'Relax,' he murmured. 'You're doing very well. And look up at me.'

She obeyed. He smiled down at her, a warm smile that made her catch her breath. His hand suddenly seemed to burn through the light silk of her dress. She glanced away, trying to remind herself he was only pretending. The thought stiffened her spine. She looked back up at him to find his eyes fixed on her face.

'That is better,' he said softly. 'I prefer to see your face, not the top of your head. Although it is very charming.'

'Indeed.'

'Yes, although I suspect you do not believe me.'

'Are all your conversations so ridiculous?'

'I am afraid so. But I am willing to reform if you so desire.'

'I really have no desire to reform you in any way.'

'But isn't that the task of a fiancée?'

'I should hope not. In your case, I think it would be quite impossible. I would never attempt it.'

'I believe I might enjoy being reformed at your hands,' he said lazily.

'Perhaps, then, you could start by ceasing to flirt with me.'

'You are undoubtedly correct. I am not certain I could reform if that is your condition. I must admit I enjoy it too much.'

'Have you ever attempted a serious conversation?'

He grinned. 'On occasion. Do you have a topic in mind? Plato's *Republic,* perhaps, or the political ideology of Edmund Burke?'

'Those topics are a bit too serious for a ball. You could start with more mundane subjects…the weather, or perhaps a remark or two on the company.'

'Are those what most men you dance with discuss? They must either be complete fools or blind. I can think of much more interesting things to say when I'm holding a lovely woman in my arms. Did you know your hair is touched with flame under the candle light?'

She looked away, flushing. Why couldn't she turn his compliments away with a cool smile or witty repartee? Instead she behaved like a young miss out of the school room.

He said nothing more and the waltz finally came to an end. He guided her towards the edge of the room, then looked down at her.

'There you are!'

Lady Hartman bounded up next to them. She bestowed a delighted smile upon Rosalyn. 'I had to come and properly congratulate you. I was so astonished last night—you must think I was terribly rude.'

'I quite understand. It must have been a horrible shock.'

Caroline laughed, and her dark eyes so like her brother's sparkled with pleasure. 'Oh, not a horrible shock! A wonderful shock once Giles—my husband, that is—explained who you were.' She glanced at Stamford. 'Perhaps you could go and fetch some glasses of lemonade? I wish to talk to Lady Jeffreys without you hovering about.'

'I trust you are not planning to malign my character.'

Caroline sent him a teasing smile. 'Oh, not at all. I shall just tell her about all the horrid things you did such as putting mice into our beds and...'

His brows snapped together. 'Has Giles ever considered locking you up?'

'Oh, all the time. Do go away! I promise I won't say anything...at least now.'

He gave her a warning glance and stalked off. Rosalyn watched in fascination. Caroline turned to her with an impish grin. 'He can be quite impossible—in fact, he is most of the time. But if one only knows the right things, he is remarkably easy to provoke. I shall give you a few hints.'

'I really don't wish to provoke him.'

Caroline patted her arm. 'Oh, but you will. Particularly when he is behaving in his most top-lofty fashion. Come and sit by me for a bit. I know of a little alcove.'

Rosalyn followed her, genuinely liking Caroline. Despite her outspoken manner, she possessed a warm heart. Rosalyn had never considered she might actually like his family.

Caroline nodded at acquaintances. They stopped once, and Caroline introduced Rosalyn to a small group of ladies who could not quite hide their curiosity under polite smiles.

They turned away, Rosalyn nearly stepping into a lady behind them. The apology died on her lips when she encountered Lady Marchant's icy stare. Stunned by the anger she saw, Rosalyn looked away.

They finally made their way to a small niche in a room connected to the ballroom. They seated themselves on the sofa.

'How surprised everyone will be when your betrothal is announced,' Caroline said. 'I can scarcely wait! I do wish you would marry right away, but Aunt Margaret says you wish to wait until the autumn. I must admit it will be good for Michael to cool his heels a bit. He is used to women falling over themselves to do his bidding. If I were you, I would make him wait until winter. He should be quite compliant by then. Don't you think a Christmas wedding would be nice?'

Rosalyn choked with a laughter she had not felt for an age. 'I am not sure half a century would be enough time,' she said shakily, trying to imagine a compliant Lord Stamford. 'He does not seem very biddable.'

Caroline merely laughed. 'Oh, you'll manage him very well.'

Caroline began to talk of their family. By the time Lord Stamford arrived with two glasses of lemonade, Rosalyn felt as if she was beginning to know them very well. There was a younger brother, Philip, who had been at the Congress in Vienna with Castlereagh, and had been in Europe forever, but was soon to arrive home. Their younger sister, Julianna, was to be presented next year. She found out their mother had died when Michael was scarcely twenty, and his father had been very much in love with her.

Lord Stamford handed Rosalyn a glass. 'I hope Caro has not talked your ear off.'

'Oh, no. She has told me all about your family.'

'I see.' His expression was unreadable. 'Perhaps you won't mind if I steal Rosalyn away. Giles is looking for you, at any rate.'

'Oh, is he? I dare say he wishes to dance with me. We are most unfashionable in that regard.' Caroline squeezed Rosalyn's hand. 'I will leave you to my brother, then. Will you be home the day after next? I should love to call on you.' She flitted off, leaving her lemonade on the window seat.

'I hope Caroline did not overwhelm you overmuch.'

'She didn't a bit. I liked her very much,' Rosalyn said warmly.

He looked at her for a moment. 'I am glad.' But she really could not tell if he was pleased or not. He touched her arm. 'Will you stand up with me again?'

'It is not necessary for you to dance attendance on me all evening. Surely we have spent enough time together to satisfy everyone.' She stared at her lemonade, feeling rather awkward.

'Trying to rid yourself of me again?' He sounded rather angry.

She looked up at him, surprised. 'No, I just thought you might wish to do something else.'

'What I wish to do is dance with you again.'

'Oh.' She twisted her hands together. 'Thank you, then.'

He took her arm and led her through the room which had become increasingly crowded. As they reached the doorway, a woman stepped back into Rosalyn, knocking her arm.

Her lemonade spilled down the front of her bodice. 'Oh!'

'I beg your pardon.' Lady Marchant's lovely face showed feigned surprise. 'Why, Lady Jeffreys, is it? How very clumsy of me! I am terribly sorry!' She suddenly seemed to notice Lord Stamford. 'Why, my lord! What a surprise to see you here! I thought you detested balls!'

By now several people had turned to stare at them. Rosalyn was mortified. Her glass had been nearly full and she could feel the liquid seeping through her shift. 'Tis no matter.' She glanced up at Stamford. His face was expressionless, but she could sense his anger.

'Please, perhaps we could find my grandmother.' She wanted nothing more than to escape before there was some sort of scene.

'Of course.' He escorted her from the room and into the ball room, then released her as soon as he found a vacant space near the wall. The dancers were executing the steps of a quadrille. 'Damn! Rosalyn, I beg your pardon,' he said stiffly.

'There is no need. You did not knock into me,' she said in a feeble attempt to reassure him as he looked completely at sea.

'No, but I've no doubt she purposely did it.' He scowled. 'I am afraid it is rather noticeable. Do you wish to find a more private room and see if it could be dried?' he asked doubtfully.

She sighed. 'I think it is hopeless. I rather think I should like to go home.'

'Of course. I will escort you.'

She looked at him swiftly. 'That isn't necessary.'

'It is the least I can do. Don't fight me on this.'

She waited while he collected her cloak. To her consternation, Lady Carlyn declined to accompany them, merely sending a message that she would call on Rosalyn tomorrow. Lord Stamford said little, however; his thoughts seemed to be elsewhere. And when he escorted her to her door, he only bowed over her hand, then seemed to think of something. 'I will call on you tomorrow. I will also see that you have a replacement for your ruined gown.'

'What?'

But he had already departed.

Chapter Six

Rosalyn finally gave up and pushed the letter aside. She had spent the morning struggling to explain to her dearest friend, Lucy, the Countess of Darmont, why she had entered into such a hasty betrothal. Particularly since Lucy had always teased her about her cautious nature.

She rubbed her temples. She'd slept little after last night's ball, making it all the more difficult to concentrate. Perhaps if she walked in the park she'd feel more alert.

'My lady?' She looked up from her desk to see Mrs Harrod standing in the door of the library. 'You have a visitor. Your brother.'

'James?'

'I'll show myself in.' He pushed past Mrs Harrod, who took one look at his livid face and beat a hasty retreat.

Rosalyn stood. 'James? What is wrong?'

'What is wrong? Are you out of your mind?' he shouted.

'I beg your pardon?' For the first time she could

remember in years, he had an expression on his handsome face besides a closed, sulky indifference.

He took a deep breath, his fists clenched at his sides. 'Stamford. He called on me to announce he intended to marry you.'

'Oh, dear.'

'I can't say you seem surprised. My God, I had no idea you'd ever met the man! Then I hear some blasted rumour you were at the opera with him and now he's wanting to marry you!'

Rosalyn knotted her hands together. 'I had meant to tell you myself.'

'You're telling me this is true? He has asked you to marry him?'

'Yes, it is true.'

'And you're planning to accept him?' His dark hazel eyes were filled with disbelief. 'Are you in love with him?'

'I am very…very fond of him.'

'Fond? I don't believe you! He's not the sort of man you would ever consider, not after John. Stamford is a rake! A libertine! Some of the stories I've heard. And he has our estate.' He stared at her as if hit by a sudden thought.

'He said he would return Meryton. Something about it being a family matter.' His eyes were full of accusation. 'You're doing it to save Meryton.'

'I…I am not.'

'You are. Blast it, Rosalyn! How can you interfere like this! I told you I would take care of it! You are not going to marry him!'

'You cannot dictate to me, James. I will marry him,' she said quietly.

'You've lost all reason. Has he seduced you? If he has I vow I will kill him.' His voice held a distinct threat she had never heard before.

'No, of course he has not.' She stepped towards her brother, holding out her hand imploringly. 'James, please listen to me.'

He refused her hand. 'The man has cast some sort of spell over you. I only pray you'll come to your senses in time. I, for one, have no intention of accepting your marriage.'

He turned and stalked towards the door. He wrenched it open and then paused and looked back at her. 'I will never take Meryton back with Stamford as my brother-in-law!' He closed the door softly, a sound more ominous than if he'd actually slammed it.

She sank back down on the chair behind her desk, willing herself not to cry. She had never dreamed he would guess why she became betrothed to Lord Stamford. And she had never expected such anger. Indifference, scorn, perhaps, but not this. For years she'd watched him shut away his emotions and now anger had erupted from him like the sea crashing through a wall.

The familiar wave of helplessness she experienced when it came to Lord Stamford washed over her. She had planned to break the news to James herself. Instead, Lord Stamford, in his usual high-handed manner, had taken care of that.

Tears welled up in her eyes, and spilled over. Never had she felt so completely defeated in her entire life.

The day was perfectly beautiful; the park glittered with that particular dewy freshness that came with the

sun after a night of rain. A herd of cows grazed peace-
fully at one end of the park. Three urchins and a
shaggy black and white dog were occupied with a
stick and hoop. A couple, clearly in love from the fond
gazes they threw each other, strolled down one of the
paths.

These bucolic delights were lost on Michael. He
reined his gelding, Faro, to a stop, his eyes searching
for his affianced. When he finally spotted her purchasing a nosegay of violets and cowslips from a small
girl, he swore. What the devil was she doing in Green
Park without her maid?

He'd come to call on her, only to have her housekeeper inform him Rosalyn seemed a trifle overset and
left for a walk in the park. He had no idea what had
upset her, but he was determined to find out.

He waited until Rosalyn had started back down the
path, a petite figure in a pelisse of dark violet and a
high poke bonnet, before he urged his horse into a trot.
He halted beside her.

'What in the devil are you doing?' he inquired sardonically.

She gave a little jump and stared up at him. He
could have been Satan himself from the look of consternation that crossed her face.

'Doing? I…I am talking a walk.'

He swung down from his gelding and caught the
reins. 'It is quite improper of you to be strolling
around in the park without your maid. Do you have
no sense of propriety? This is hardly the country where
such conduct might be acceptable, but the middle of
London.'

'I know perfectly well what I am about, my lord.

You need not concern yourself with my behaviour. My abigail had a headache today so of course I would not ask her to accompany me.'

'You could ask a footman.'

'My footman has other business to attend to.'

An exasperated snort escaped him. 'Then, in that case, I suggest you forgo your walk.'

'If you have interrupted my walk merely to lecture me on propriety, then I suggest you leave. You are wasting your time, my lord,' she replied with stiff dignity. She turned her back on him and moved away, her head high.

Her prim accents and attempts to keep him at arm's length filled him with the most wicked desire to flirt with her unmercifully.

He caught up to her. 'That was not my chief reason for calling on you. I wanted to discuss our betrothal, my love,' he replied softly, pulling her arm through his, drawing her closer to his side.

He was gratified to see the action noticeably confused her, causing the pink in her cheeks to intensify.

'I am not your love, my lord. I pray you will release my arm.'

'Only if you will address me by my given name.'

'This is most ridiculous, my l—Michael,' she replied.

'My Michael?' he drawled, raising a satirical brow. 'That is certainly some improvement over "my lord." Does this mean you hold me in some affection after all, my dear Rosalyn?'

She yanked her arm out of his, stopped on the path and turned to face him. He was delighted to see her eyes flash and her cool composure melt. Her fist closed about the small bouquet of flowers, causing them to wilt.

'That is not what I meant, as you very well know!'

'Really? I am disappointed. What did you mean?' he inquired.

'Can we please stay with the matter at hand?' she snapped.

'You seem rather out of sorts for a lady about to receive an offer,' he remarked blandly.

'I am not about to receive an offer! Why must you always be so odious!'

To his astonishment, her lip quivered and tears welled up in her large eyes. She quickly turned her head.

The lone tear trailing down her cheek, which she wiped away hastily, had an instant sobering effect on Michael. Feminine tears usually inspired little emotion in him besides exasperation, but he felt an overwhelming sense of guilt that he had gone too far.

'My dear girl, I did not wish to make you cry,' he said.

'I...I am not crying.' She sniffed and another tear rolled down her cheek.

'Yes, you are,' he insisted softly. 'Look at me.'

She shook her head, refusing to face him. 'I...I never cry.'

He gently touched her averted cheek. 'Of course not. But I can see you are overset. Can you not tell me what is wrong? I am sorry if I have teased you too much. My sisters have often flung that accusation at me.'

'There is nothing wrong. I would like to return home, if you please.'

She brushed ineffectively at the tears that were now freely falling. He fumbled in his pocket for a hand-kerchief and handed it to her. Taking her arm in a firm grasp, he led her under the spreading branches of an oak, his horse following obediently behind. He dropped the reins and caught both her hands in his. Her nosegay fell to the ground.

'What has you so blue-devilled, Rosalyn?'

She finally raised her head. Her eyes searched his face. She drew in a deep breath. 'It is James. He called on me, and he was so angry. He said he did not want Meryton. I…I had wanted to tell him about our…our betrothal myself.'

'Is that it? I did not mean to cause you more distress by going to your brother. I thought to save you some trouble by telling him myself that my intentions were honourable. I thought, too, you would want to know I intended on keeping my side of the bargain.'

She sniffed again and dabbed at her eyes with the handkerchief. 'I…I see. But…but he doesn't want Meryton if I…I am betrothed to you.'

He touched her cheek. 'But you want it.'

'Y…yes.'

'Do not distress yourself too much, he will come around. I will see to it.'

'Thank you, then,' she said quietly and gave him a shy smile. For the first time in their brief acquaintance, he nearly found himself at a loss for words. He was suddenly aware of the clean light scent she wore, a mixture of lavender and roses, and of how very soft and pleasing her small gloved hand felt in his.

An unexpected bolt of desire shot through him. He dropped her hand as if it burned him and then could have cursed himself for the startled expression on her face.

'I believe I should escort you home,' Michael said, running a distracted hand through his hair. He avoided touching her as she fell into step beside him. Faro trailed along behind.

He cleared his throat. 'I had something else I wish to tell you, which is the other reason I wanted to settle the matter with your brother. I will be going to Eversleigh for a day or two to see my father. He has summoned me. I believe he wants a first-hand account of our, er…relationship.'

'Oh, dear.' She shot him a quick look. 'Do you think he will be angry?'

'No.' His father's brief note had been surprisingly cordial, although it was a summons none the less.

'I hope not.' She continued to watch him with that faintly puzzled look as if she didn't know what to make of him. Michael hardly knew what to make of himself—he felt as unhinged as if he were actually about to ask for her hand.

'Well, shall I go down on my knee and declare my sentiments? I have not done this before.'

'Whatever for?'

'I have not made you a proper offer.'

'It is not necessary since we are not really to be married. You should wait until you meet the lady you wish to marry. It would also be best if you waited until you are in a drawing room before going down on your knees. In the midst of a public park with a horse at one's heels is not the most convenient place to make such an offer.' To his surprise, her eyes shone with gentle laughter.

He grinned back at her. 'And probably not the most romantic, either.'

They reached the steps in front of her townhouse. Michael paused and looked down at her. 'By the way, there is something else you should know. I told your brother he was not to gamble again until his debts were paid off.'

Her hand closed around the locket she wore. 'But why? Is that necessary?'

He frowned. 'Yes. Does that distress you? It should not. He must learn that it's foolish to gamble what he does not have. Particularly when he possesses such little skill.'

A flash of anger showed in her eyes. 'So it is acceptable to gamble when one is wealthy and skilled, then? Is that the philosophy you follow, my lord?'

The censure in her tone rankled him. 'Of course, my lady. I am extremely fortunate to lay claim to both.'

'I see. So what happens if he does gamble again?'

'I will take possession of the estate.'

She stared at him with disbelief. 'But you are changing the terms of our bargain! You said nothing of that before!'

He smiled coolly. 'Not at all. What good will it do to return the estate to him if he either stakes it again or is forced to sell it to pay off his debts? Is that what you want to happen?'

'No. You are right,' she said softly.

Her admission should have given him a small victory. Instead, he felt angry. 'I will see you in a day or two, my dear.' He looked down into her flushed face and was filled with the unwelcome desire to pull her to him and kiss her hard. With a muffled curse, he turned and strode away.

Rosalyn gazed at the closed door, completely bewildered by his behaviour. She had obviously angered him, but surely not so much that it would make him look as if he wanted to strangle her.

Even more confusing was his kindness before that. The rueful apology in his eyes when she'd expected mockery had thrown her off completely.

Still puzzling over his behaviour, she slowly made her way to her drawing room and sank down on her sofa.

She put a hand to her head, which was beginning to ache. For the first time since she had braved his drawing room, she saw him as something other than an enemy. She had glimpsed another side to him, a side that was kind and understanding. A side that was much more frightening than that of the charming rake she knew.

Two days later, Rosalyn stood in her bedchamber staring with more than a little dismay at the hat boxes and packages strewn across her bed. Any idea she'd had of spending the two days away from Lord Stamford in quiet solitude had been dashed the instant her grandmother had shown up in her drawing room shortly on Stamford's heels. With grim determination on her face, Lady Carlyn had announced that no granddaughter of hers would be marrying a Marquis looking like a governess.

So Rosalyn had spent the last two days in a whirl of visits to milliners and dressmakers. Not to mention shopping for gloves, fans, slippers, and stockings. She was exhausted. And she dreaded to see the bills. James would not be the only one in debt, she reflected wryly.

James. She idly picked up a bonnet trimmed with sea-green ribbons, a frown creasing her brow. She hadn't heard from him since the day he'd come to call and had been so angry about her betrothal. She had visited his rooms, but he had not been in. After waiting for over a half an hour, she'd finally given up and left a message.

Her grandmother had brushed aside her worries. 'My dear, he has probably gone off with one of his friends. Young men are like that.' They had been sitting in her grandmother's Chinese drawing room taking tea.

'But he was quite angry with me when I told him about my betrothal. He…he thinks Lord Stamford is a rake.'

'Of course, he is a bit wild, but that makes him much more interesting. I was fond of John, and I never wanted to say a thing, but he was, well, a bit dull. Particularly for such a young girl as yourself.'

'I loved John,' Rosalyn had said stiffly. 'I never found him dull.'

Lady Carlyn had patted her hand. 'I know, dear. But it was a respectful sort of love. With Lord Stamford it will be quite different.'

'I hardly think so.' Rosalyn was hurt and insulted that her grandmother would make such an unfavourable comparison between John and Lord Stamford.

Her grandmother had smiled in a knowing manner. 'You won't be able to escape it, my dear. I have seen how he looks at you. Which brings me to another point. I have no idea why you have this harebrained notion about delaying the wedding.'

'I don't want to be married so soon. We hardly know each other.'

'At least you might consider Lord Stamford's wishes in the matter. I cannot imagine he wishes to wait until autumn. It is quite foolish of you to make a man of his passionate temperament cool his heels too long!'

'A man of his passionate temperament? Whatever do you mean?'

A loud, exasperated sigh escaped Lady Carlyn. 'Must I spell it out for you, dear? You are a widow, you should know that men have certain needs, however inconvenient they may be for a woman. I do not think he wants to wait that long, not with the way he watches you.' She stared at Rosalyn with speculative eyes. 'Unless, of course, you already have…'

'Grandmama! I would never do such a thing!'

'There is no need to look so shocked! You are not exactly an innocent young girl, and it would hardly raise an eyebrow as long as you were discreet. I have heard from several sources that he is most pleasing to women in that regard! You are certainly the object of much envy.'

'I cannot believe anyone would ever speculate on such a topic. This is most dreadful!' exclaimed Rosalyn, truly shocked and completely mortified.

'Of course they do, dear. Most of society does not share the same scruples as you.'

Even now, the memory of that conversation made her blush. Unbidden, a vision of lying in his arms, his dark face hovering over hers, that teasing half-smile on his face, as he lowered his lips to hers…

Her knees went weak. She jerked her thoughts away from such a disturbing image. Of course, she had no interest in him in that way. He was the most handsome man she had ever encountered but also the most aggravating and arrogant and…

'My lady, you have a visitor,' Mrs Harrod said, interrupting her thoughts.

Rosalyn started and put the bonnet back in its box. 'Who is it?'

'Mr Fairchilde.' Her housekeeper's voice was stiff. 'Are you at home?'

'I…yes. I will be there shortly.' She had no real desire to see him, but perhaps he'd know James's whereabouts.

Mrs Harrod bustled off with a disapproving snort. Rosalyn removed her pelisse and bonnet, which she realized she was still wearing, and, after straightening her locks, reluctantly made her way to her drawing room.

He sat on her striped sofa, long legs stretched before him. He rose at her entrance, his size shrinking the room. He was dressed in buckskin breeches and a light blue coat which made the steely grey of his eyes more noticeable.

His smile was cool and appraising. 'Lady Jeffreys, how good of you to see me. I called once before, but you were not at home.'

She gave him her hand, resisting the urge to snatch it away and smiled diffidently. 'I have been out with my grandmother. Please, sit down.' She seated herself on the nearest chair and folded her hands in her lap wondering nervously what he wanted.

'Have you seen James?' she asked, trying to think of something to say.

He shrugged. 'Not for several days. That is not why I called.'

He sat back down, his eyes fixed on her face. 'I will not dissemble. I was surprised to see you at the opera the other night with Lord Stamford.' His voice was light, but there was an underlying edge in it that made her uneasy.

'We are acquainted.'

'But how did he ever persuade you to accompany him? I will own I was quite envious of his position, having you at his side. But are you certain it was wise? His reputation is not the most sterling. In fact, his taste for lovely widows is quite well known. I should hate to think of you falling under his spell.'

'I assure you there is no need to worry about that,' she said stiffly.

'Good. He would be a most unfaithful lover.' His gaze drifted over her in a way that made her nervous.

'I...I have no idea what you are talking about.'

'Don't you? He has your brother's estate, and you are quite lovely. Perhaps he hasn't made you an offer yet, but I've no doubt of his intentions.'

She rose, trying to keep her voice calm. She longed to throw her betrothal in his face, but it was not yet public knowledge. 'You have no idea of his intentions. And I certainly would never think of becoming his mistress, if that is what you are saying. I pray you will leave, sir.'

His gaze was unfathomable. 'I have something to

discuss with you. Your brother's debt. I am quite willing to loan him the money for repayment. At a reasonable interest. I might even be persuaded to forgive him the small loan I have already made him.'

'What is his debt? I have a little money of my own.' She had no idea James owed him money. She was beginning to feel slightly sick.

'I was not talking about money. There are other things you could do to make the terms even more reasonable.'

'Really.'

'Yes, my lovely Rosalyn. Come to Vauxhall with me tomorrow, and we can discuss the terms.'

'Vauxhall? I have never cared for Vauxhall.'

'Then come and dine with me.'

'Dine with you? No, I cannot.'

'If you want your brother's estate back, then you will.' He also rose, and looked down at her, a hardness in his gaze that made her afraid.

Suddenly, she knew what he wanted. How could she be so stupid? She backed away from him. 'You are mistaken if you think I will agree to that.'

'There is no need for these games, my dear. I know why you accompanied Stamford to the opera. It is as good as agreeing to his terms, even if he hasn't yet offered them in so many words. But I can offer you much more pleasure than Stamford ever will.'

She glanced towards the door. At least she was in her own home. If she screamed, Mrs Harrod would come running. 'No! He has offered me nothing like that.'

His hand shot out, and for a moment, she thought he meant to grab her. Then he dropped his hand and smiled coolly. 'Hasn't he? Then I am certain that is what is on his mind. Not that I blame him. I have wanted you, desired you, since that first time I saw you at Meryton.'

Fear and revulsion coursed through her. 'Please, say no more. I want you to leave.'

'As you wish, my dear lady. I am persuaded that once you think about it you will reconsider. Your brother is in my debt, and I do intend to be repaid.'

She backed out of the drawing room then, almost tripping over Mrs Harrod, who stood at the door with a militant look on her face, broom in hand. Rosalyn had no doubt her loyal housekeeper meant to use it on Fairchilde if necessary. Rosalyn fled up the stairs, to the sanctuary of her bedchamber. She closed the door, and leaned against it, taking deep breaths to calm herself. Her concerns had always been for James and Meryton. Now she felt more than a little frightened for herself.

Chapter Seven

Three days later, Michael entered Rosalyn's small study. Occupied in arranging a vase of flowers, she did not notice him until he was nearly behind her. She jumped, dropping a stalk of delphinium. 'My lord... Michael, I did not expect you back so soon.'

He retrieved the flower and handed it to her with a smile. She looked different today. Instead of the pale blues and greys she usually wore, her dress was white muslin patterned with swirls of flowers. Her hair was pulled back and arranged in soft tendrils around her face. She looked soft and fresh and utterly charming. He experienced the sudden urge to touch her soft cheek. His voice came out more abrupt than he'd intended.

'I just returned last night.'

'Oh.' She moved around the table and tucked the delphinium in the vase, then looked at him. 'But Caroline said Eversleigh Hall is nearly a day's journey away.'

'That is true. After I saw my father, I found little point in remaining.' He had tried to convince himself he merely wanted to return so his father wouldn't suspect something was wrong, but now the truth hit him. He had wanted to see her.

'You must be exhausted. Was he very angry?'

'No, not at all.' He smiled briefly. 'He has given his consent to our marriage.'

'Our marriage?'

'I mean our betrothal. Amazingly, he had no objections.' Which had puzzled Michael greatly. He had expected arguments, but instead his father had seemed quite pleased. Michael had nearly reeled with shock.

A faint suspicion entered his mind that something was afoot, but he could hardly bring that up with his father.

'Didn't he? I am glad it was not too difficult for you.'

'No.' He moved away from her, not looking forward to telling her the next item of news. 'There is just one complication, however—he wishes me to bring you to Eversleigh.'

'Eversleigh? Oh, no! I…I really do not want to meet your father.' Then she flushed. 'That is, I am certain he is very nice…but, I…'

His mouth quirked. 'There is no need to explain. More than one man has been known to tremble at the prospect. But don't worry, I'll try to fob him off as long as possible.'

'Thank you.'

'I will put the announcement in the *Morning Post*. I believe our betrothal dinner is tomorrow?'

'Yes.' She looked uncomfortable. 'I wish your aunt had not decided to hold a dinner. I feel so dishonest!'

'I fear it is part of a betrothal. Caro informs me we were fortunate it was not a ball.'

She sighed. 'Could we have not had a secret engagement?'

His lips twitched. 'That would have spoiled the purpose for contracting the engagement in the first place.'

He pulled a small jeweller's box from his waistcoat pocket and stepped to her side. 'I have something for you. My father wanted me to give it to you.'

He held the box out. Her eyes flew up to his face as she hesitantly took it.

She removed the lid. Inside the box lay an elaborate ring of diamonds and rubies in an ornate, old-fashioned setting. She stared at it, a stunned expression on her face.

'It's a ring, my dear.'

'I…I know. Michael, I cannot accept this.'

'Why not? It is customary to give one's fiancée a ring. It would be considered extremely remiss of me to not do so.'

When she said nothing he added, 'I know it is rather hideous. I would have preferred to give you something less ostentatious as you have such delicate hands, but I'm afraid this is a family heirloom. It is a tradition for brides to wear it. My father commanded me to give it to you.'

'No…no, it is not that. I mean it is not hideous. I am certain it is too valuable for me to wear.'

Michael laughed. 'If you were Caroline, I might worry about your losing it. But I am sure it is quite safe with you.' He held out his hand. 'Give me your hand, Rosalyn. I'll place it on your finger.'

'I must remove my wedding ring first,' she said with

a slight tremor in her voice. Her dark hair hid her face from his sight as she slowly slid the plain gold band from her left hand. She looked at it for a moment before placing it on her other hand. He thought she looked rather sad. For the first time since he'd struck the bargain with her, he felt a twinge of remorse over forcing her into it.

He took her hand and slipped the heavy ring gently on her finger. Her soft hand trembled in his clasp.

She looked up at him. 'I will take care of it. I shall, of course, return it to you when this is over.'

'I have no doubts on that score.'

She clasped her hands together in that way she had when she was distressed.

'Is something wrong, Rosalyn? Are you worried about the dinner or my father?'

She shook her head, and then swallowed. 'It is James.'

He frowned, feeling impatient at her brother's name. 'James? Has he gambled away the estate again?'

'No, of course not. He has disappeared without any word. I have no idea where he is.'

'I see. I doubt if he's met with foul play, if that is what worries you.' Michael thought it most likely the young fool had gone off with some friends for a few days.

She looked even more anxious. 'I…I hope not. But he's never done anything like this before. I know I am probably very foolish, but I worry that something has happened. He was so angry with me. Perhaps I drove him to leave.'

Michael made an impatient sound. 'That is ridiculous. He's one-and-twenty years of age, certainly—'

'He is twenty.'

'As if that makes any difference.' He frowned at her. 'He's old enough to make his own decisions. You're not responsible for him.'

'But I am. When my mother was dying, she asked that I look after James and Papa.'

Michael had no idea whether he wanted to shake her or kiss her. 'I am certain she only meant until your brother was grown.' He stepped towards her. 'The devil! Rosalyn, there is no need for this.'

She backed away from him and sniffed. 'I pray you will go. I am sorry to have troubled you.'

'No.' He ran a hand through his hair. 'Very well. I will make some inquiries and see where he's gone.'

'I don't wish you to do that. I…I have been making some inquiries myself.'

'Without much success, I take it,' he said sardonically. 'I probably have a better idea where he might have gone than you do.'

'It is not necessary for you to involve yourself in our…our lives,' she said with stiff dignity.

He raised a brow. 'Whether you like it or not, I am very much involved, my dear.' This time when he came towards her, she had no place to retreat since she was backed up against the wall. He touched her cheek. 'Don't look so worried. Your brother will be fine.'

She raised startled eyes to his face, looking like a doe that was about to flee. Her breathing grew shallow. 'Th…thank you,' she whispered.

'Not at all. Rosalyn…' he said hoarsely. He bent towards her, knowing he had to kiss her.

'Oh, my lady, I beg your pardon!'

Michael's head jerked up at the sound of the house-keeper's voice. Rosalyn's hand flew to her throat. 'Wh…what is it?' she said.

Mrs Harrod, her face slightly red, came into the room. She was followed by the footman carrying a huge bouquet of flowers. 'These arrived for you, my lady. Where do you want them?'

Rosalyn stared at them as if she had never seen a flower before. Then she seemed to come to life. 'In the drawing room, I suppose. Who sent them?'

'I do not know. Here is a card.'

Michael watched as she took it, and waited until Mrs Harrod had departed with the flowers, before speaking. He folded his arms. 'Another admirer, my dear?'

'Oh, no. I don't have any admirers,' Rosalyn said distractedly. She opened the card, and read it. He watched as her face turned pale.

'Who are they from?' he inquired.

She looked up, a rather sick look on her face. 'No…no one. That is, just someone I…I knew. It is nothing.'

He held out his hand. 'Give me the card.'

'No!' She whipped it behind her. 'Please, Michael.'

Now what? She looked so distressed, he didn't want to press her. However, he had every intention of finding out who would send her flowers that would make her look so upset. And then he'd put a bullet through the man.

The intensity of the thought shocked him. He'd never felt the least urge to fight a duel over any woman in his life. In fact, he'd never been the least bit inclined to put himself out for any woman, except for perhaps his sisters. And now this petite widow, with the large hazel eyes, was embroiling him in her concerns.

No. He was embroiling himself.

This time it was Michael who backed away, putting distance between them. 'I will take my leave of you, Rosalyn.' His voice was unnaturally stiff for one of the *ton*'s most notorious flirts.

'Very well.' She gave him a confused little smile.

She followed him to the door of her study. He turned and looked down at her. 'I will let you know what I find out about James.'

'Thank you. You are very kind.'

'Hardly.' Pulling his eyes away from her mouth, he turned abruptly on his heel and left.

A few inquiries at Fallingham's was all Michael needed to discover James had gone to the races at Newmarket with several of the wildest young bucks in London. Michael only hoped James decided to forgo any wagers, but he thought it highly unlikely.

Michael was about to leave the establishment, when a soft voice spoke from behind him. 'I fear you got the worse of the bargain when you took on the estate of James Whitcomb.'

Michael turned and met the hooded gaze of Edmund Fairchilde. His hackles rose. There was something about the man's tall, broad-shouldered figure and craggy face that never failed to arouse his worst instincts. Perhaps it was because Fairchilde reminded him of a watchful predator on the prowl for an unsuspecting victim.

'I hardly think so.'

'Obviously you have not seen the place, then. It is

small and in dire need of all sorts of improvements despite Lady Jeffreys's efforts to maintain it. I doubt if it is worth the vowels it was to cover.'

'Perhaps not, but I fail to see why it is any of your concern.'

'But it is. I am quite willing to offer you the sum of young Whitcomb's vowels, plus something in the nature of interest for the mortgage.'

'Why?' Michael demanded bluntly.

Fairchilde smiled gently. 'I will not dissemble. I have little interest in either Meryton or Whitcomb. But there is something else. In fact, I believe we share a common interest.'

It took only seconds for Fairchilde's meaning to penetrate and then shock jolted through Michael. 'You are referring to Lady Jeffreys?' His voice was cold.

'Yes.' Fairchilde still smiled, but his gaze was hard. 'I have had an interest in the lady for some time. I must own I was rather displeased to see her with you at the opera.'

'Were you?'

'Yes. I do not like competition. Particularly when my opponent holds such an unfair advantage.'

'So you are hoping to buy the advantage yourself?' Michael could barely keep the sneer from his voice.

'Of course. I cannot see what it matters to you. She is hardly the sort of woman you favour. You have left her unattended for several days, and I have it from a…er, reliable source that you have not yet purchased the lady's favours.'

'That is because I have no intention of purchasing them.' Michael's gaze was deadly. 'The lady in question is betrothed to me.'

He had the satisfaction of watching displeasure flit through Fairchilde's eyes. Then a quizzical half-smile curled his lips. 'How very interesting. I beg your pardon, my lord.' He executed a neat bow and walked off, leaving Michael staring after him.

Michael quit the establishment, paying little heed to his surroundings. He settled into his carriage, his mind in a whirl. Fairchilde was interested in Rosalyn? The notion of the man touching her made him ill. He had heard rumours of Fairchilde's sexual habits and they involved perversions that could turn the stomach of the most jaded of men.

And he was ruthless. He was not above using force if he wanted a woman. With sudden clarity, he knew exactly who had sent Rosalyn her unwanted bouquet.

Rosalyn's stomach churned with nervousness as she and Lady Carlyn followed Lady Spence's butler up the elegant staircase to the drawing room the next evening.

'My dear, there's no need to look as if you're about to mount the gallows,' Lady Carlyn whispered loudly as they approached the tall double doors.

Rosalyn clutched her fan tightly, trying to keep her hand from trembling. 'I am just a little nervous. I don't like being the centre of attention.'

'There's nothing to it. Just smile and don't spill soup on your gown.'

Lady Carlyn took her arm, almost dragging her into the drawing room. Rosalyn stopped, wondering if it were too late to run. A small dinner party? There must be at least thirty people in the drawing room. A quick look around the room revealed Michael was not one of those present. She found herself wishing for his support.

Lady Spence broke away from a lady with whom she had been conversing to greet Rosalyn and Lady Carlyn. She embraced Lady Carlyn, then turned to Rosalyn. 'How lovely you look, my dear,' she said warmly as she noted Rosalyn's dark pink silk. 'What a pretty colour on you.'

Taking Rosalyn's arm, she said, 'I want you to meet our other guests. I don't know where your fiancé is. He hasn't shown up yet which is so very typical. I hope you can influence him to put in an appearance on time.'

Lady Carlyn bustled away to talk to an elderly lady in puce, leaving Rosalyn to fend for herself.

Lady Spence introduced her to the other guests; a bewildering number of relations whose names Rosalyn could only hope she would recall, and several old friends of the family.

They finally stopped in front of a dark-haired young man with features that seemed familiar. He stood with Michael's cousin, Charles, and Charles's fiancée, Miss Markham. They both smiled at her in welcome.

Lady Spence brought her forward. 'Rosalyn, may I present Lord Philip Elliot, Michael's brother? Philip, may I present Lady Jeffreys? Philip has only arrived in town today. I believe you know he has been travelling on the continent.'

Lord Philip's warm grey eyes surveyed her face with lively curiosity for a moment and then he said, 'My pleasure, Lady Jeffreys. You cannot conceive my surprise when I arrived today to find my brother is to be married at last.'

'No more than the rest of us,' Charles said with a grin.

Philip laughed. 'I understand you met him only a few weeks ago. He tends to make up his mind quickly when he knows what he wants. I am afraid you hadn't a chance, Lady Jeffreys.'

Elizabeth smiled up at her fiancé. 'Then there are some men who need a bit more prodding.'

Charles looked unabashed. 'Oh, I knew what I wanted. Just didn't know if you'd agree.'

'At any rate, welcome to the family,' said Philip. He smiled at her. Although he was not as handsome as his brother, she saw he possessed the same easy charm. He held out his hand.

She no sooner had taken it, smiling at him in return, when Lord Stamford's voice spoke behind her, causing her to jump. 'I see you have met my fiancée, Philip.'

Philip released her hand. 'Yes. She is lovely. Under the circumstances, I am surprised you were not on time for once.'

Rosalyn glanced up at Lord Stamford and he smiled at her, a warm intimate look. She was momentarily thrown into confusion until she remembered it was part of the role he played. She tentatively smiled back at him. He took her hand and slowly raised it to his lips. An odd tingle shot through her body at the soft pressure.

'I meant to be, but one of my horses strained a hock. Otherwise, nothing would have kept me from your side,' he said, gazing into her eyes.

'I see.' Rosalyn was embarrassed that he should speak to her like this in front of the others. She prayed the butler would announce dinner. Whatever was taking so long?

Lord Stamford appeared about to say something when there was a sudden lull in the conversation. Everyone's head seemed to swivel in the same direction. Rosalyn, too, turned to look.

Entering the drawing room was the most beautiful girl she had ever seen in her life. From the top of her golden curls to the tips of the dainty white slippers peeking from beneath her simple white gown, the young lady who glided into the room was perfection. Large violet blue eyes shone from a face with a complexion that could truly be described as porcelain. Her slender figure with its graceful curves was only enhanced by the simple gown.

She appeared perfectly unaware of the effect she had on the assembled company as she greeted her hostess with a soft pretty smile. The other two ladies, an older woman in a lavender gown and a younger lady dressed in cream and lace, were hardly noticed in the beauty's wake.

'Who is she?' asked Lord Philip who appeared as dazed as any man in the room.

'Miss Helena Randall,' Charles replied.

Miss Randall? The lady to whom Stamford was to have been betrothed? Rosalyn's mind was in a whirl. She had tried to imagine Miss Randall and had envisioned a pretty, but naïve, young girl from the schoolroom with the giggling manners so many girls in their first season displayed. She had never thought Miss Randall would be a composed beauty who walked like a young goddess. If Stamford had known…he surely would not have suggested this sham. She stole a quick glance at her fiancé, expecting him to be gazing at Miss Randall as besotted as anyone.

Instead, to her utter confusion, his unsmiling eyes were fixed on her.

Chapter Eight

Rosalyn smiled at Lord Philip who was seated to her right at dinner. 'Will you be in England long?'

'Permanently, I hope.'

'Your family will be glad of that.'

He slanted her a half-smile reminding her of Michael's. 'Perhaps. Well, at least at first,' he amended.

She picked up her wine, thinking she liked Michael's brother very much. They had talked a little of his travels and of her husband's writing. He had read several of John's essays.

Taking a sip of wine, she stole a glance down the table at Michael. His unsmiling gaze met hers, the same one he'd fixed on her during most of the dinner. In fact, he almost was glowering at her. She flushed and dropped her eyes. Was she doing something wrong? Or did he find fault with her appearance?

Seated between Philip and Charles Portland, she had found the dinner less of an ordeal than she had expected. Both were easy conversationalists. To her surprise, she actually enjoyed herself. But it was quite apparent Michael did not feel the same.

A short time later Lady Spence stood, signalling for the ladies to depart, leaving the men to their port and conversation. She led them upstairs to the drawing room. Rosalyn sat down on a brocade settee next to Caroline and across from Miss Randall.

With her impish grin, Caroline immediately began to tease Miss Randall. 'Dear Helena, I'm afraid you've added another heart to your collection. Poor Percy Milhurst has fallen at your feet! What shall you do with all your admirers?'

Miss Randall looked alarmed. 'Oh, dear. I...I did nothing to encourage him. And he said such odd things, I could not understand half his conversation.'

'What sort of odd things? I hope he said nothing improper, Helena!'

'Oh, no! Of course not! He kept talking about my hair and eyes and comparing them to spun gold and lakes. And he offered to dedicate a poem to me. It was very tedious. His conversation is not at all sensible.'

Caroline bit back a laugh. 'No, it never has been. But how many young men have you met with sensible conversation? I imagine their wits must leave their heads when they see you.'

Miss Randall blushed and looked uncomfortable, and Rosalyn suddenly felt sorry for her. It was obvious she had no desire to be the reigning beauty of the Season with a horde of young men constantly at her side.

Miss Randall turned to Rosalyn and smiled shyly. 'I have not yet congratulated you on your engagement. I hope you will be very happy.'

'Thank you.' Rosalyn smiled back at her.

'Will you live at Eversleigh after your wedding? It is one of the most beautiful homes I have ever seen. The gardens are so lovely,' Miss Randall continued.

Rosalyn was startled. 'I really do not know. We have not discussed it.'

'I imagine you will. Unless Michael wishes to keep you to himself for a while,' Caroline said, casting Rosalyn a mischievous glance. 'He has a very small estate in Cornwall that would be most romantic.'

Rosalyn could feel a blush rise to her cheeks, which was completely ridiculous. One should only blush if one was in love with the man in question. Hastily she asked Miss Randall if she was fond of gardens.

'Oh, yes.' Miss Randall looked rather wistful. 'I miss my rose garden at home.'

Caroline excused herself, saying she must speak with her aunt. Miss Randall stayed with Rosalyn, telling her about her garden and home, and asking Rosalyn about London. Rosalyn could not comprehend why Michael would object to marriage with such a lovely girl. Perhaps now that he saw Miss Randall he would change his mind. For some reason, the thought brought her little joy.

She looked up to find Michael standing next to them. Engrossed in conversation, she had not heard the men enter the drawing room. He greeted Rosalyn and then turned to Miss Randall. 'I hope London is to your liking, Miss Randall.' His voice was polite.

'Oh, yes. Everyone has been very kind.' She smiled but Rosalyn could see nothing in her manner suggesting she regretted the loss of Lord Stamford as a potential husband. She rose in a graceful movement. 'I must speak to my cousin, if you will kindly excuse me.'

Rosalyn looked away, not certain what to say. 'Miss Randall is very lovely and quite charming.'

'I am delighted,' he said coolly. 'You seemed to be enjoying yourself at dinner.'

'Oh, yes. I very much like your brother. He has so many interesting stories about the places he has travelled.'

'Does he?' His voice was so terse, she stared at him in surprise.

'Is something wrong?'

'No,' he snapped. He looked at her for another disconcerting moment, and then frowned. 'I've located James.'

'Have you? Where is he?'

'He is at the races at Newmarket. He went with Lord Coleridge and several others.'

'Lord Coleridge?' Rosalyn's spirits which had been momentarily lifted, fell. Rodney Coleridge was a dandy and a wastrel and hardly the sort of young man she wanted James to be with. But what had she expected? 'I see. Thank you for your trouble.'

'It was no trouble.' He continued to look at her as if he were displeased.

'Michael, is there something wrong?'

'Lord Stamford, I must have a word with you.'

Startled, they both turned to see Lady Carlyn next to them, lips pursed. She tapped Michael's arm with her fan. 'I am quite disappointed. I would have thought by now that you would have persuaded her to be more reasonable.'

Oh, no. Did her grandmother have to bring this up now? Rosalyn wanted to drop through the floor.

'Lady Carlyn, I am at a loss,' Michael said with a little bow in her direction.

'Your wedding. I cannot possibly believe you wish to wait until autumn. Not when you've been in such a hurry to bring her to heel.'

'Grandmother, please,' said Rosalyn frantically.

'Well, it is impossible to do a thing with you. I thought perhaps Stamford could talk some sense into you. She never knows what is best for herself, particularly in these matters.'

Michael glanced at Rosalyn's face, which was by now hot with embarrassment. He looked bemused. 'If you'll excuse us, I would like to have a word alone with Rosalyn.'

'Of course,' replied Lady Carlyn, flashing Rosalyn a triumphant smile.

He led Rosalyn to a small study near the drawing room and closed the door, then turned to face her. 'What the devil is that all about?'

She avoided his eyes. 'It is nothing to signify. She cannot fathom why we don't wish to marry right away. I cannot persuade her we would rather wait until autumn.'

He looked completely astonished.

She smiled slightly. 'Don't worry, my lord. I plan to cry off at the appropriate time. I have no intention of marrying you in the autumn or any other time.'

'I have no fears on that score, my dear. I am quite aware of your thoughts on the subject.' His voice was so cool, she flushed.

Then a rueful smile lifted his lips. 'I supposed it

never occurred to me we would actually be asked to consider a wedding date.'

She sighed. 'Nor did I. Not until Lady Spence brought it up. She and my grandmother thought a wedding in six weeks would be most appropriate.'

He stared at her. 'Six weeks! Good lord! What did you say to that?'

'I was so taken aback I hardly knew what to say. I told Lady Spence I would prefer autumn as it is my very favourite season. The leaves are so pretty, you know,' she said with a wry smile.

'Of course. Did she accept that?' he asked. His mouth twitched.

'She had no objections. But Grandmama does not like it. She thinks we should be married immediately. She is horribly tenacious once she gets an idea in her mind. One is almost compelled to do as she wishes just to be left alone.'

'Riding you pretty hard, is she?'

'Yes.'

'Don't trouble yourself about it any further. I will handle your grandmother.'

'No, I cannot let you do that.'

'Why not?'

'It is just…' She floundered, not knowing quite how to explain how she felt. 'I don't want to hide behind you.'

'Hide behind me? What in the devil are you talking about?'

'I am not completely helpless. I have been managing Meryton. And before that, I managed my husband's household. I am perfectly capable of controlling my grandmother. I don't want you to interfere in everything I do.'

'I'm not trying to interfere. I am trying to make this situation easier for you.'

'There is no need to do so.'

'I am responsible for you.'

Her mouth fell open. 'Responsible for me? Whatever gives you that idea?'

'You are betrothed to me. Therefore, you are my responsibility.'

'I am not betrothed to you! I am pretending to be betrothed to you.'

He scowled and folded his arms across his chest. 'I will not argue that point with you again. You are my fiancée until we sever our agreement. I will do as I see fit in these matters, particularly those that concern our betrothal.'

'You mean you intend to high-handedly interfere in my life.'

'If that is how you want to see it, yes, I intend to do so.'

'Well, really! I have nothing more to say to you.' She marched towards him, intending to stalk out of the study with as much dignity as possible.

He caught her wrist before she could pass him, pulling her around to face him. 'But I have more I wish to say to you.'

She glared at him. 'Is this how you intend to treat your fiancée? Forcing her to listen to you by imprisoning her?'

He stared down at her, anger and frustration clearly showing in his face. Suddenly a cool smile lifted his lips. 'You are right, there are more effective ways.'

Before she could even think, he yanked her hard against him, his mouth imprisoning hers. Stunned, she offered little resistance until his mouth softened on hers, sending shivers down her spine. Her mouth parted and his tongue lightly touched hers. She pushed against his chest, panicked by her own reaction.

He released her, staggering a little, his expression unreadable.

She backed away, her hand groping for the door-knob. Without a word, she wrenched the door open and fled.

Michael thrust the paper aside. Impossible to concentrate on the damned thing. The only item that caught his interest was the announcement of his betrothal. The sight of his name coupled with Rosalyn's was unnerving. He read it over at least five times.

Of course, it meant nothing. It was, after all, a false betrothal as Rosalyn kept reminding him.

And after last night, he would do best to remember that. He nearly groaned. Whatever had possessed him to kiss her again? He could still recall the taste of her sweet mouth, and the feel of her soft curves pressed against him. The memory had kept him awake a good portion of the night.

And then there had been the blasted dinner last night. He'd never been jealous of his brother before, but he was as he watched her smile and talk to Philip with an easiness she'd never displayed with him. It had occurred to Michael that Philip was exactly the sort of man she would prefer. And when she'd innocently told him how much she did like Philip, it was all Michael could do to keep himself from forbidding her to so much as glance at his brother.

Undoubtedly, it had been too long since he'd been with a woman. Some latent sense of honour kept him from taking another woman to his bed as long as he was betrothed to Rosalyn. And after last night, he was finally forced to admit, only one woman aroused more than a passing interest in him—his reluctant fiancée.

He shook himself. Involving himself with Rosalyn in any other way than business was pure folly. From now on, he'd keep his distance.

He threw the paper down and stood up, then started at the sight of Elinor Marchant in the doorway, her demeanour cold. His butler stood behind her, his face frozen in icy disapproval.

'Elinor, what a surprise,' Michael said coolly. 'And to what do I owe the pleasure of this visit?'

'Dear Michael! I have not seen you for an age!' she exclaimed, holding out her hand. The cold look disappeared, to be replaced by a charming smile. She was elegantly dressed in a pomona green gown topped by a matching pelisse trimmed in white braid. The green of the gown brought out the lovely jade green of her eyes. The low cut of her dress, almost breaching propriety, showed a tantalising glimpse of her full breasts. Michael had once found her semi-scandalous mode of dress exciting, but now he found himself comparing it to Rosalyn's prim gowns. He found he much preferred his betrothed's more restrained style of dress.

'An age? That is something of an exaggeration, since I saw you only the other night when you so conveniently backed into Lady Jeffreys.'

Elinor opened her eyes very wide. 'An accident as

you surely know. Tis so crowded at these affairs.' She laughed, a low throaty laugh, and moved to touch his arm. 'You know that is not the same. I mean we have not—really seen each other.' It was impossible to mistake her meaning.

'No. I believe you made it clear last winter that you wished to sever our relationship,' said Michael bluntly.

'You mean our little quarrel? It was only a lover's tiff. I never thought you would take it seriously,' said Elinor with a little pout.

'If a lady says she never wants to see me again and wishes me to perdition, I, of course, do not question her meaning,' said Michael. He had been relieved when Elinor quarrelled with him. The stormy relationship with the dashing widow had begun to pall on him, and her departure to the north after violent words during a ball had saved him the trouble of giving her her *congé*. 'But rehashing this is meaningless—what exactly is the purpose of your visit?'

'Why, I read the most amusing thing today. I had to come to verify it for myself.'

'And what is that?'

'The announcement of your betrothal to that quiet little creature, Lady Jeffreys. I could not believe my eyes! Tell me it is not true.'

'Very true. I sent the announcement myself.'

'But how very odd! Marrying one of your flirts? Really, Stamford, whatever possessed you to do such a thing!'

Her tone was light, but the tight lines about her mouth betrayed her inner fury.

'For all it is your business, I find nothing odd in the

fact I have decided to marry,' said Michael coldly. 'And Lady Jeffreys is hardly one of my flirts.'

'Really? I thought you never had any intention of marrying. And then to marry such a dull creature. She is so old! She must be at least thirty. I would have been less surprised if you had announced your engagement to a schoolroom chit. Whatever can you find to say to her? She has no conversation.'

Most of the time he reacted to Elinor's goading by pretending to misunderstand, thus turning the tables on her, but hearing her insult Lady Jeffreys filled him with cold, dangerous anger. 'I'm not sure you know what conversation is, my dear. I can't recall we had that many.'

Two spots of red appeared on her cheeks. 'Is that why you've decided to marry her? You can't get anything but conversation any other way! What a sly little thing she is. I am surprised you would be caught so easily by such wiles. Although I could almost feel sorry for her; marriage to you will be unbearable when you tire of her!'

Michael stepped towards her and Elinor involuntarily took a step back. Fear flickered in her face. 'If you were a man, I'd call you out for that remark,' he said softly, coldly. 'As it is, I suggest you leave. You may show yourself out. I will not trouble Watkins with you. And by the way, I trust there will be no more accidents to Lady Jeffreys's person.' He turned his back to her in dismissal and picked up the paper.

When he heard the door open, he looked up in time to catch the look of hatred which distorted her lovely features as she glanced back at him. She then turned on her heel and left, slamming the door behind her.

Michael stared at the closed door with an uneasy feeling. He knew Elinor's temper and capacity for revenge. The maliciousness beneath her lovely façade was one among several other undesirable qualities that made him glad to be rid of her. But what could she possibly do? He did not think she planned to murder Rosalyn or him for that matter. He dismissed Elinor from his mind.

Lady Marchant burst into her cousin's breakfast room, causing Edmund Fairchilde to grimace. He put down the cup of coffee he was about to put to his lips and raised a lazy brow. 'My dear Elinor, whatever brings you here? And in such a temper so early in the day! I cannot recall what I have done to offend you.'

'Nothing, Edmund. I must speak to you. I want your help!'

'My help? How intriguing. But do sit down, I cannot finish my breakfast with you pacing like that!' He motioned her to sit across from him. Elinor seated herself and pulled off her gloves in short angry strokes.

'Now, what has put you in such a towering rage?' he inquired.

'Stamford is to marry that creature!' exclaimed Elinor without preamble. 'How could this happen? I thought you wanted her!'

'I still do. But what is the problem? I thought you were finished with his lordship.' When she said nothing, he regarded her speculatively for a moment. 'Did you actually hope to be the next Duchess of Eversleigh?'

'Why not? Was it so impossible?'

'It was a long shot, my dear, even if you had played

your cards right. But I'm afraid your last scene at the Oxford ball ruined your hand. Damning your lover to hell and throwing vases in public is not good *ton*, my dear.'

Elinor glared. 'And I suppose the proper Rosalyn Jeffreys would never do such a thing.'

'It is unlikely.'

'Well, I don't intend she shall ever be the next Duchess, either!'

'I hope you still don't have hopes in that direction, Elinor. I'm afraid Stamford is a hopeless cause. If you plan to regale me with tales of your loss, I shall ask you to leave as I find the topic quite boring.'

'I quite detest Stamford,' she replied coldly. 'I wouldn't take him back for all the gold in the world! No, it is revenge.'

'Ah, revenge,' said Edmund. He pushed his coffee cup aside. 'Now you begin to interest me. What do you have in mind?'

'I should like Stamford to find out his intended is not as virtuous as he thinks. That under that proper exterior beats a heart as faithless as any.' She leaned forward in her chair. 'I want you to break up their betrothal.'

'I hoped you would come up with something a bit more original. I quite intend to do so.'

'Well, how could you let it get this far?'

'My dear, Stamford holds the trump card. He has the estate. His lovely fiancée would do anything to retrieve that worthless piece of property for her brother.'

'So she is marrying him for the estate?'

'Possibly.'

'Can't you get it back?'

'I have already offered Stamford the price. He refused.'

Elinor scowled. 'I can't believe he wants her enough to marry her. He is a fool.'

'He may be many things, but he's not a fool. No, he has his reasons. However, they don't concern me.' He smiled in a way that made Elinor suddenly glad she was not his intended victim. 'I fully intend to bed Lady Jeffreys. Resistance only makes the game more interesting. And I will quite enjoy thwarting Stamford.'

'I have no idea what any man could see in such a mousy thing. And she is so prim,' said Elinor with a sniff.

'Sometimes the most prim ladies are the most challenging of all. They can be quite passionate beneath the proper exteriors. It merely takes the right man to bring it out.'

'Don't be vulgar, Edmund!'

'And what are your plans for thwarting this marriage, m'dear? Or are you leaving it entirely up to me?'

'I shall think of something.'

Edmund's mouth curled. 'I've no doubt you will. You know, of course, he will call me out. And I always get my man.'

Elinor shrugged. 'He never misses either. I dare say you shall be quite evenly matched and it will prove to be quite amusing.'

She was quite calm now; plans for intrigue and revenge always had a soothing effect on Lady Elinor

Marchant. She took a dainty bite out of a piece of buttered toast.

'You are a wicked woman, Elinor,' remarked Edmund.

'Me? I am not wicked. I merely do not like being insulted. I am quite nice when people are pleasant to me.'

He laughed, pushing his chair back from the table. 'I do not wish to be rude but I must go, m'dear. I have an appointment. Enjoy yourself.' He left Elinor sitting at the breakfast table, her chin propped in her hand, a secretive pleased smile on her lovely face as she plotted away.

Chapter Nine

Rosalyn shoved the pile of bills away and sighed. She feared she would go broke by the end of this betrothal. An engagement to a Marquis was turning out to be an expensive proposition. Perhaps she should present Michael with the bills and demand compensation. Except she had the lowering feeling he would probably pay them as part of the responsibility he seemed to assume for her.

A frown creased her brow. A week had passed since the dinner party. An uncomfortable week in which she and Michael seemed to be at odds with each other. After that kiss, any fears she might have entertained that he planned to pursue more intimacies with her had been put to rest by his stiff behaviour. He was perfectly attentive in company, but he acted as if she had the plague the few times they were actually alone together.

Which was what she'd wanted all along, she tried to tell herself. Guilt rushed through her every time she thought of how she had melted against him as if she welcomed his embrace. Despite the disappointments in her marriage, she had loved John. Never had she dreamed another man's kiss could temporarily make her forget him. Worse, the kisses of a man such as Lord Stamford, a hardened rake, the antithesis of all that John had been. Unfortunately, she had a difficult time remembering that.

'Rosalyn?'

She looked up. As if her thoughts had conjured him, Michael stood in the doorway. In his hands he carried a parcel. Flustered, she rose, pushing a tendril of hair aside. 'I didn't expect you today.'

He advanced into the room. 'I had no idea if you would be home.'

'I have a mound of bills to pay as you can see. I thought I should do that.'

He came to stand in front of her desk. 'Are you managing?'

'Oh, yes.' She was embarrassed as she remembered her earlier thought. Certainly she did not want him offering her money. 'I have just been putting them off. Paying bills is very tedious. Is there something you wish?'

'I have brought you a replacement for your ruined gown.'

Her eyes flew to his face. 'There was no need for that. I cannot accept it.'

He set the parcel on the desk. 'You must. I had it made especially for you with Caroline's advice. Open it.'

'But it is not proper.'

'How can you be certain? You've not yet seen it. It is a very proper gown.'

'No, I mean it is an improper gift. I cannot accept such a thing from you.'

He lifted a brow. 'Must you always argue, my dear? I wished to replace the gown that was ruined. I told you I would do so.'

'The gown was hardly new.'

'Rosalyn. Are you going to open it or not?' He sounded as if he was fast running out of patience.

He was in one of those exasperating moods where argument was futile. With unsteady hands, she undid the string and lifted the lid. Her breath caught at the sight of the lace-trimmed, pale pink satin bodice with its delicately puffed sleeves. With gentle hands, she lifted it from the box. The skirt consisted of a lacy overdress over a white satin slip. She stroked the silky material, thinking it was the most beautiful gown she had ever seen.

She looked up to find Michael watching her. 'Do you like it?'

'It is beautiful.' She laid it back in the box. 'But I cannot accept it.'

He made an impatient movement. 'If you don't wear it, then no one will. Caroline claims she cannot wear that shade of pink. And it is not suitable for my younger sister.'

'I see.' She looked back down at the gown. John had never had a gown made up especially for her. It seemed to speak of an intimacy between Michael and herself which did not exist. But Caroline had helped him. Usually men did not solicit their sisters' help in choosing gowns for a mistress, did they? Why must he always confuse her so? Nothing he did seemed to fit in the mould of proper behaviour.

'Now, what is it? Will you accept it?'

'Yes, thank you.'

'Will you wear it?'

'Well, yes.'

'Then I will expect to see you wearing it tonight.'

'Tonight?'

He raised a brow. 'Why not? You are planning to attend Miss Randall's coming-out ball, are you not? You and she seemed to have become fast friends.'

'Of course I will be there. But I had planned to wear a...a different gown.'

'You don't like it.' His voice was flat, almost as if he were disappointed.

'Oh, but I do! I don't think I have ever seen a lovelier gown.'

'Then you object to it because it is from me.'

She sighed. 'No, not precisely. It is such a personal gift. I know you wish to replace my other gown, but I cannot help but feel very peculiar about it. If I was married to you, it would be different. I would be much more comfortable if you had brought me a bouquet of flowers, or perhaps some sweetmeats. A dress seems the sort of thing you would give to a...a...'

'Lady of easy virtue?'

'Well, yes.' She coloured.

His lips twitched. 'I beg your pardon. I see we have been speaking at cross-purposes. I was merely looking at it as part of a business arrangement, and you have been worrying about the propriety of accepting a gown from a man you are not permanently attached to.'

Her mouth opened in amazement. 'What do you think I have been trying to tell you? I told you it was not a proper gift!'

He looked slightly abashed. 'I wasn't thinking of it as a gift.'

'I quite understand that now.'

'Will you wear it tonight?'

She looked up at him with a faint smile. 'Yes, if only so you won't glower at me the entire evening.'

'Do I glower at you?'

'When you want your own way. Sometimes you fold your arms and raise your brow in a particularly haughty fashion.'

'I had no idea I was so intimidating.'

'I dare say you cannot help it. I imagine it comes from your being the son of a Duke and used to having others jump to do whatever you wish.'

'A most devastating reading of my character. However, I cannot see that you jump at all to do my bidding.'

'I try not to, but in the end you generally prevail.'

He appeared genuinely surprised. 'Do I?'

'Yes, my lord, you do.' She was torn between laughter and exasperation. Sometimes, when he forgot to be so aristocratic, he actually was quite human.

Her breath caught as he suddenly levelled a devastatingly attractive grin at her. 'I can see I must do something to right matters. Would it help if I put myself at your bidding? I am completely at your command.'

'I...I fear I wouldn't know what to do with you.'

'I could think of a few things,' he suggested with a wicked smile.

'Really, my lord!' Colour rose up into her cheeks. This betrothal would be so much easier if he wasn't such a flirt and always attempting to make her blush.

'What is wrong?' he asked innocently. 'I was merely thinking of doing an errand or two, or perhaps delivering some messages. Or I could carry parcels for you.'

She shook her head, wanting to laugh. 'You are quite ridiculous! I don't think you would want everyone to think I considered you a…a sort of footman. It would ruin your reputation.'

'I wasn't aware I still possessed much of one. However, it would be worth losing what little I have in order to see you smile at me like that.'

'Oh.' The smile faded from her face, as awareness flared between them. She looked away from his suddenly intent gaze, confused by the emotions he was arousing in her.

'I will be off, then.' His now cool voice made her look up. He picked up his gloves and with a slight nod, strode away without another word.

By the time Rosalyn arrived with Lady Carlyn, the ball was in progress. They had been late due to a misplaced necklace Lady Carlyn was determined to wear, followed by a spot on her cloak which necessitated looking for another wrap. Nearly an hour had passed by the time they were underway. Rosalyn would have been happier to stay at home, but she did not want to miss Helena's ball.

After they were announced, Lady Carlyn declared her intention of joining some friends in the card room. Rosalyn drifted towards the edge of the ball room to stand near a group of matronly chaperones in turbans and headdresses. She wore the gown Michael had brought. The fit was perfect and, as she had viewed

herself in the looking-glass, she was forced to admit
she had never had a gown more becoming. The soft
pink colour set off her dark hair and made her pale
ivory complexion glow.

Much to her relief, Lady Carlyn hadn't asked where
she had purchased the gown, merely saying she had
never seen her look so charming. Rosalyn wondered
if Michael would think the same, then mentally shook
herself for caring what he thought.

Where was he anyway? She searched the crowded
ball room and finally spotted him leading Helena on
to the floor for a quadrille. His dark head bent towards
hers as he spoke, and she responded with one of her
lovely, unaffected smiles. The music began. Helena
danced as gracefully as she did everything, moving
through the steps with Michael as if they were made
for each other. And they looked charming together,
Rosalyn thought with an odd pang.

She turned away, sudden fatigue washing over her.
Perhaps she would join her grandmother in the card
room. She started to make her way there, only to be
stopped by an acquaintance of Caroline's, and then by
a friend of her grandmother's. She finally escaped only
to nearly slam into Lady Marchant who was leaving
the card room.

'I have never properly congratulated you on your
engagement,' Lady Marchant said. She ran her eyes
over Rosalyn as if hoping to find some fault with her
appearance.

'Oh?' Rosalyn gave her a polite smile and attempted
to move past her.

Lady Marchant also moved, neatly blocking her escape. 'How did you ever manage such a coup as to

persuade Stamford into marriage? He has been extremely adept at evading the matrimonial trap all these years. Everyone is quite amazed that you managed to pull it off. And in such a short time.'

Rosalyn looked into the lady's coldly smiling face. So many people had said the exact same thing to her since her engagement, she was suddenly out of patience. As if she had trapped Michael into this betrothal, particularly when circumstances were so much the opposite. She was tired of smiling politely at the notion that it was such a miracle she had managed to bring him to heel.

'That is not precisely how it happened, Lady Marchant. I did not persuade Michael to marry me, he persuaded me to marry him. I really had no intention of ever remarrying, but Michael can be very persistent when he wants something.'

A flash of anger quickly came and went in Lady Marchant's eyes.

'Really? That is more in Stamford's style. He always enjoys the hunt, but I should warn you that once he catches his prey he becomes bored. Until that point he can be very charming. I'm not certain he would make the most comfortable of husbands, but perhaps you know what you are about.'

'I quite understand Michael.'

'Do you? Then perhaps you aren't quite as naïve as you appear. As long as you are willing to overlook his indiscretions I am certain he will allow you yours.'

Rosalyn stared at her, outraged. 'I have no intention of being unfaithful to my husband.'

Lady Marchant's smile held disbelief. 'Then you will undoubtedly spend many a night alone.' She gave a little laugh. 'My dear, I did not intend to distress you, merely warn you. Of course, when a woman is lying in his arms he is skilled at making her believe she is the only one. I know.'

'But then, he is marrying me.' Rosalyn was pleased to see her shaft hit home. Lady Marchant's smile vanished. 'If you will excuse me.'

Rosalyn turned on her heel, but not before she saw the malice in the lady's green eyes. She entered the card room, searching for her grandmother. Her small triumph faded when she realized she had undoubtedly made an enemy. She suddenly felt bone-tired.

Lady Carlyn, engrossed in her game, paid scant heed to Rosalyn's presence, except to ask if she cared to join them. Rosalyn, whose skills extended only as far as jackstraws, declined. She finally grew tired of watching and drifted away, wishing she could call the carriage and leave.

She wandered back to the ball room. She did not see Michael anywhere in the crowded room.

Someone touched her arm. 'Lady Jeffreys.'

She swung around to find Lord Philip behind her, elegantly dressed in a dark blue evening coat and black pantaloons. He smiled. 'My brother has been looking for you all evening. Has he found you yet?'

'No, I have not yet spoken to him. I've been in the card room.'

He laughed. 'I believe he was under the impression that was one place you would not be found.'

'Most of the time he would be right.'

'If you wish to find him, he is out on the terrace. Now that he has dutifully danced with Miss Randall, I don't think he'll dance with anyone else until he finds you. Not that I blame him,' he added, his eyes sweeping over her with admiration.

She suddenly felt happy. 'Perhaps I will go to the terrace, then.' She smiled at him, and after promising him a dance, made her way through the guests to the doors leading to the terrace.

A cool breeze brushed her cheeks as she stepped through the French doors. Lanterns spaced along the low wall terrace wall cast a dim light. She stood for a moment, letting her eyes adjust to the dark. A few couples strolled in the small garden below and a group of men stood in one corner of the terrace, their laughter carried on the night air.

She drifted in the opposite direction, not certain where she would find Michael. Perhaps looking for him was a stupid idea. Then, as she approached a large urn filled with flowers, she heard his voice. She stopped when she saw two figures in front of her, only partially hidden by the urn.

'Damn it, did you have a reason for accosting me or not? I'm in no mood for these games,' Michael was saying.

'Dear Stamford, I hated to see you here by yourself, brooding in such a poetic fashion. It is quite unlike you. But then you have hardly been yourself.' Lady Marchant's velvety tones were unmistakable.

'This is nonsense.'

'I dare say it is due to your charming fiancée.' She moved towards him. 'She certainly keeps you on a tight rein. I'm surprised you've not yet bolted.'

Even in the dark, Rosalyn felt her face go hot. She had no desire to hear Michael discuss her with his ex-mistress or, for all she knew, his present mistress.

She started to move away, but she must have made a slight sound. Elinor glanced over Michael's shoulder. Her eyes narrowed for an instant and then she draped her arms deliberately around his neck. 'My love, I knew you'd come! Tell me you miss me as much as I miss you!' she exclaimed in a voice rather loud for true intimacy.

Rosalyn froze. Mesmerised, she watched Michael struggle to remove her hands from his neck. 'What the devil! Elinor, let go of me!'

'No! No! Not until you kiss me, my darling!'

'Are you mad?' Elinor attempted to drag his head down. Michael tried to shove her away. Elinor clung to him like a cat with its claws caught. Rosalyn gasped as he staggered backwards into the urn. He cursed. Elinor abruptly let go.

Then he saw her. 'Rosalyn?' He looked as if he'd just swallowed a vial of poison.

'I…I beg your pardon. I see you are occupied.' Her face hot with embarrassment that he had seen her, she turned and hurried away.

Inside the ball room doors she stopped, hit with the insane desire to laugh. Had Michael been engaged in a tête-à-tête with Elinor Marchant, or had she actually been attacking him? Perhaps she should have stayed and defended his virtue.

'My dear, I have been looking for you all evening.'

She spun around. Edmund Fairchilde stood at her side, a lazy smile on his lips.

'Indeed.'

'I had hoped to speak to you, perhaps steal a dance with you.'

'I can't imagine why you would think I would consent to do either after the last time we met.' She started to edge away, only to find his hand closing around her wrist.

'I understand you are looking for your brother.'

'He is at Newmarket. Please release me.'

'He was at Newmarket. He is no longer there.'

She stiffened. 'How would you know?'

He let her go. 'I am very interested in your brother's whereabouts. He owes me money, you see. I always see to it my debtors pay. Come and dance with me and we can discuss this matter.'

A little smile played about his mouth, making her think of a predator about to close in for the kill. She looked around, but no one paid them the least attention. For once, she wished Michael would suddenly appear.

As if reading her mind, Fairchilde laughed. 'I fear your fiancé is otherwise occupied. Which is one reason I wanted to talk with you now. He is a trifle possessive, is he not?'

'How much does my brother owe you?'

'Dance with me and I will tell you.'

'I don't care to dance.'

'If you want to hear about your brother, you will.' There was no mistaking the veiled threat in his voice.

With a sickening feeling, she allowed him to lead her to the ball room floor with the other dancers. Too late, she realised the dance was a waltz. 'I...I don't waltz very well. Perhaps another dance?'

'I don't believe that, not when you do everything else with so much grace.'

He pulled her on to the floor, his arm circling her waist. His breath smelled unpleasantly of brandy and tobacco. She held herself stiffly away from him, but his fingers only tightened.

He looked down at her. 'You look particularly lovely tonight. The gown brings out the colour in your cheeks.' His gaze drifted down lower, and she had the sudden urge to tug her bodice up to her chin.

She said nothing.

'It is noble of you to sacrifice yourself for Meryton. But are you certain it is worth it? I fear tying yourself permanently to Stamford will bring you nothing but unhappiness.'

'I wish to speak of my brother. How much does he owe you?'

'Two thousand pounds. But do not trouble yourself, I have no doubt his debt will be paid.'

Two thousand pounds? That was half of her income. And how much did James owe elsewhere? She looked up into Fairchilde's hooded gaze and shivered. 'Do you know where my brother has gone?'

'I don't wish to discuss your brother now. I would rather admire you.'

She tripped, stepping on his foot. His eyes hardened, and his fingers tightened at her waist.

'You are holding me too close for propriety, sir!'

'Am I? I fear having you in my arms makes me forget myself.' He did not loosen his grip.

Feeling trapped, she looked around trying to reassure herself that nothing could possibly happen in the middle of a ballroom. And then she saw Michael.

He stood near the French doors, his eyes searching the room. They fell on her. Even from across the room, she could see him stiffen. Then he pushed past a group of ladies.

She had no doubt he was coming towards them.

She glanced away, her stomach twisting in knots.

'Did I tell you how lovely you look tonight?' Fairchilde whispered.

'I…I don't feel well. I need to sit. Please!'

Fairchilde raised a disbelieving brow. The next moment a hand closed on his shoulder, yanking him back. He nearly stepped into a whirling couple, causing the lady to let out a shriek.

'I suggest you keep your hands off my fiancée,' Michael snarled. He looked as if he was about to do murder. Although the music continued, most of the dancers near them had by now halted, their fascinated gazes on the two men.

Fairchilde raised a lazy brow. 'I was merely dancing with her. Surely you cannot object to that?'

Michael stepped forward and took Rosalyn's arm in a viselike grip. 'I do object. If you come near her again, I will call you out.' His voice rang out in the ballroom which had suddenly gone completely quiet.

'This is…is most ridiculous. Michael, please.' Out of the corner of her eye, she could see her grandmother's mouth open in a horrified circle. Next to her stood Lady Jersey. For the first time in her life, Rosalyn wished she could swoon dead away.

'Lady Jeffreys is right. Do you plan to call out every man she dances with or is it only me? She did agree to stand up with me. I did not force her.' Fairchilde's eyes glinted.

Michael glanced down at Rosalyn, his mouth tight. 'I wish to speak with you in private,' he said.

His dictatorial tone, combined with the humiliation

of having the entire ballroom watching, set her back up. How dare he take her to task in front of everyone?

She raised her chin. 'But I don't wish to speak to you, my lord. Please release me, you are hurting my arm.'

Colour tinged his cheekbones, but he instantly dropped her arm. She marched away from him past the crowd of fascinated guests.

She barely registered Lady Marchant standing nearby, her eyes glittering with malicious pleasure. The musicians chose that moment to strike up the next dance, causing the assembled group to disperse. Heedless of the others, Rosalyn dashed towards the tall double doors leading out of the ballroom.

Her grandmother caught up with her when she reached the hallway outside the ballroom. 'Whatever possessed you to dance with Fairchilde? Oh, dear! How could you! This is most dreadful! I never thought to see you involved in such a scene!'

To be blamed for the whole thing was the last straw! She lifted her chin and stared straight at Lady Carlyn. 'I would like to go home. Now!'

Lady Carlyn's mouth fell open, and then she closed it abruptly. For once in her life, she made no argument.

Chapter Ten

Rosalyn set her plate of toast and marmalade aside. Eating seemed pointless, particularly when the food refused to move down her throat. After last night, she doubted if she'd ever survive this nightmarish Season. She'd either collapse from lack of sleep or lack of food.

What ever had possessed Michael? Nearly brawling with Fairchilde and threatening a duel. Then speaking to her as if she were at fault in front of the entire *ton*.

Every time she thought of his high-handed behaviour, she cringed. How dare he? Especially after that scene with Lady Marchant, whatever that had been about! For all she knew, he had been having a rendezvous with the lady, not that it meant a thing if he was. If she had any courage, she would send his ring back with a curt note telling him their bargain was off. Except, he might think she cared what he did, which, of course, she did not.

Well, she had more important worries than the arrogant Lord Stamford.

Such as what to do about James. She pushed her

chair back and crossed to the window, staring out at the street. Despite the sun shining through the window, she felt cold. If he was not at Newmarket, then where was he? Had he fled from his debts? She could not believe he would do such a dishonourable thing.

Two thousand pounds. Meryton made enough to cover the mortgage and the wages of her servants, but there was not much left over. Somehow, Fairchilde must be paid. The memory of his touch made her flesh crawl. She was protected now with her betrothal, but what would happen when it ended? And what if he threatened James?

She leaned her head against the wooden shutter. Asking her grandmother for the money was out of the question. Lady Carlyn usually borrowed heavily on her income. Not to mention the awkward questions and unwarranted advice. She'd never let her grandmother know the extent of the debt her father had left. Lady Carlyn had never forgiven Lord Frederick Whitcomb for stealing her daughter away from his older brother, the Marquis of Wrotham, as she saw it. No matter that they had been blissfully happy.

Perhaps her solicitor could be persuaded to make her an advance on her income. Her glance fell to her wedding ring.

She still had her jewels.

'My lady! Look what has just arrived for you!'

Rosalyn looked up. Mrs Harrod stood in the doorway, peering around a huge bouquet of pink roses she held. She beamed. 'So lovely, they are!'

She waddled into the room, the heavy scent of roses filling the room. 'And here is a card and a small box!'

Rosalyn looked at them with trepidation, praying it

was not another bouquet from Fairchilde. She took the card and opened it.

'Please accept my sincerest apologies.' It was signed in Michael's dark, sprawling hand.

'And this, my lady? Shall you want to see what's inside?' Mrs Harrod thrust the box at Rosalyn, her face eager.

Rosalyn gave the card back to the housekeeper. With trembling fingers, she lifted the lid of the box. Inside lay a gold brooch in the shape of a rose, its delicate petals glistening in the sunlight streaming through the window.

'How lovely!' Mrs Harrod exclaimed, peering around the bouquet she still held.

'Yes, it is,' Rosalyn said slowly. It was beautiful, the sort of jewellery she had always preferred, simple and elegant. And she loved roses. She hardly knew what to think, and then reminded herself it was only a gesture to keep a temporary fiancé in line. He undoubtedly had sent hundreds of gifts to women in his lifetime.

'Shall I put some roses in here? And perhaps some in the drawing room?'

'Yes, of course. That would be lovely.'

Mrs Harrod bustled away to find a vase. Rosalyn stared at the brooch, touching the delicate petals with one finger. How ironic that, just as she had decided to sell her jewels, Michael should send her such a gift.

She laid the brooch back in its box. She would return it to him, of course. As for now, she'd best go before she lost her courage.

Three hours later, Rosalyn returned. As she entered the house, Mrs Harrod informed her Lady Spence had just arrived and was in the drawing room, taking tea.

'She said she would wait a bit for your return,' Mrs Harrod said, taking Rosalyn's pelisse and bonnet.

'Oh, dear.' How could she possibly face Michael's aunt after last night?

But when she entered the drawing room, Lady Spence rose to greet her with all her usual warmth. She held out her hands. 'My dear girl, I had to see how you were faring after last night. I hope you are not too overset.'

Rosalyn took her hands. 'I am so sorry.'

'But why? It was hardly your fault that Michael decided to quarrel with Fairchilde in public. I dare say you had no idea they quite detest each other.' She sat back down, drawing Rosalyn down beside her.

'No. Oh, dear. I really did not wish to dance with Fairchilde but…' her voice trailed off. She could not tell Lady Spence why she had felt obligated to dance with the man.

'Of course not.' She patted Rosalyn's hand. Her eyes held a twinkle. 'It is probably quite dreadful of me, but I must own I was rather pleased to see Michael become so angry.'

'Were you?'

'Oh, yes. He is always so horribly indifferent to everything, I have sometimes wondered if anything ever affects him. How splendid to see him stalk forward and threaten to call Fairchilde out! Particularly in the middle of a ball room! Certainly there was nothing indifferent about that!'

'No,' Rosalyn said weakly. The resemblance between Lady Spence and her niece was suddenly quite apparent.

'And you handled him very well. I was quite pleased to see you did not let him force you to go with him. Walking away from him was just the thing to do. I have always feared he would decide to marry some meek, worshipful creature who would obey his every word.'

'I…I see.'

'I hope you will not be too hard on him for last night. I think he fears you may not wish to speak to him after the way he spoke to you in such a high-handed manner.'

'You have seen him?'

'Today. I suggested he call on you, but he wasn't sure if you would receive him.' She leaned forward and smiled at Rosalyn reassuringly. 'He really does care for you, my dear. He is rather like his father in that he tends to become most overbearing with those he cares for most.'

Rosalyn felt a deep blush cover her face. Of course, he did not, but why must he carry the charade this far? Interfering in her life, threatening duels and convincing his family he cared about her.

She didn't want that! Any more than she wanted to care about him. She moistened her lips, trying to think of something to say since Lady Spence was looking at her expectantly.

'Of course I will speak to him,' she finally said.

Lady Spence smiled. 'I had no doubt. You are a sweet girl. Michael is very fortunate.' She leaned forward and kissed Rosalyn's cheek, then stood. 'Now you must rest. You look rather pale. Poor child, I fear this has all been most tiresome for you.' She tied the strings of her bonnet, then looked at Rosalyn. 'Oh, yes, will you be attending Almack's tonight?'

Rosalyn also rose, her mind a blank. Almack's? She had quite forgotten she was to go with her grandmother. 'I believe so.'

'Very good. Then you will see Michael there. By the way, Caroline is planning a little houseparty for next weekend. Three days, I believe. It shall be a perfect time for you and Michael to be away from London, particularly in light of last night.' After giving Rosalyn a quick hug, Lady Spence departed.

Rosalyn sank back down on the sofa and rubbed her head. A houseparty? As usual after dealing with a member of Michael's warm, but overpowering family, she felt completely lost.

The thought of a night at Almack's made her groan. She supposed she must go, if only to prove to society she and Michael had not seriously quarrelled. On the other hand, she was feeling quite out of sorts with society's dictates. She really wanted to do nothing more than curl up at home and read one of the Gothic novels she'd borrowed from the circulating library.

Other ladies had headaches. Rosalyn had never stooped to using a feigned one in her life, but there was always time to start. Why not tonight?

She was tired of the pretence, tired of trying to keep her life in control. Tired of worrying about James. She wanted to escape.

With great resolution, she marched to her desk in the library and pulled out a piece of stationary. Nothing was going to drag her from her house tonight.

* * *

Michael entered Almack's, a place he never set foot in except under extreme duress.

The only reason he had come was to see Rosalyn. His aunt had assured him of her presence. But after scanning the ball room, then making his way through the other rooms, he saw no sign of her. He returned to the ball room. A young lady in a white muslin gown trimmed with yards of muslin and lace cast him a flirtatious smile. He scowled, and she fled.

'Poor Michael!' He looked down to see Caroline smiling up at him, mischief dancing in her eyes. 'I never thought to see you so lovestruck. Pacing the floor, waiting for your beloved. Why, just now, Lady Jersey was remarking on how tame you've become, with the exception of last night, of course. She said that could only be put down to how far gone you are.'

He raised a brow. 'I am hardly lovestruck, my dear.'

'And cross! That is another sign. Men are always cross when they're in love.'

No scathing remark leapt to his mind, unless he wanted to deny he was in love with Rosalyn. But since he'd fully intended to create the impression he was, he'd only be cutting his own throat. How in the devil had he gotten himself in this muddle?

Caroline glanced towards the door. 'Lady Carlyn has just arrived. But I don't see Rosalyn with her. I do hope nothing is wrong, Aunt Margaret was quite certain she would be here tonight.'

He nearly bolted from Caroline and made his way across the room to where Lady Carlyn stood with his aunt. Was she ill or merely avoiding him?

Lady Carlyn eyed his approach with a disapproving expression. 'I suppose you wish to know where

Rosalyn is. She is at home with a headache. A headache! She has never had one in her life! I dare say it is all because of that business last night.'

'She looked quite pale when I saw her earlier,' Lady Spence said. 'I have no doubt she is not particularly well. Although I had hoped she would be here, as I fear her absence will be noted.' She gave Michael a cool glance. 'I take it you did not deliver your apology in person.'

'I sent her flowers and a note,' he said stiffly. He had no idea why he felt it necessary to defend his actions.

'I suppose that was a start,' Lady Carlyn said. 'Although I think she must be quite overset. She was not receiving any visitors when I called. Her housekeeper informed me she was resting. I have never known her to rest during the day! I remember when I visited her when John was alive. She had the most severe cold. She insisted on seeing to the household management even though it was obvious she was quite ill.'

'Confound it,' Michael said. He scowled. 'Very well, I will call on her now and apologise. Does that please you?'

'Michael! Really!' Lady Spence exclaimed. 'This is hardly the time!'

'I only hope she will receive you,' Lady Carlyn added.

'She will.' He gave them a baleful glance and stalked out.

Rosalyn stared down at the pages of her novel, *Bungay Castle*. Unfortunately, the trials of the heroine failed to distract her from her own troubles, which seemed just as complicated as poor Roseline's, only not quite as improbable. With a sigh, Rosalyn closed the volume.

She glanced up at the clock ticking on the mantel. The hour was nearly eleven. Perhaps she should go to bed, but because of her long afternoon nap, she no longer felt tired.

The rap on the door startled her. Who would be calling at this hour? She rose, setting her book aside, and pulled her shawl more firmly about her shoulders. She was dressed in an old cream gown and had not bothered dressing her hair, only tying it back from her face with a ribbon.

She heard Mrs Harrod's voice outside the drawing-room door, then a very familiar masculine voice. She froze. Whatever was Michael doing here? She had an absurd desire to hide, but unless she dived behind the sofa, she hadn't a prayer. The door opened. He came into the room. One look at his dark, forbidding face made her wish she had hid.

She stood. 'My lord! What you doing here?'

He scowled at her, the low light of the lamp making him look even more saturnine in his evening clothes. 'I could ask you the same. After waiting for you at Almack's, I was informed by your grandmother that you were so overset by last night's ball you had taken to your bed.'

'Why ever would she say that? I was resting when she called but that was merely because I slept rather poorly last night, and then I did not...' Her voice trailed away at his raised brow. No doubt he was angry because she was not keeping up the pretence of dutiful fiancée very well. 'I am sorry. I should have gone to

Almack's, but I was terribly tired and the thought of another assembly with everyone staring, then trying to smile and talk as if nothing mattered, was too daunting. I thought I would stay home and read.'

He moved into the room. 'And you did not see fit to inform me? After last night it was imperative that we be seen together.'

'Perhaps, but I am not accountable to you for my every move. And I was not the one who chose to create such a…a ridiculous scene. If you are here to rip me up about that, then I would like you to leave.'

'I have no intention of ripping you up.' He took a step towards her and stopped. 'Damn! You are right. I came here to apologise to you, and instead I behave badly. It was only…' He paused and frowned at her. 'Will you accept my apology for causing you such distress last night?' he asked stiffly.

'Yes, of course.' She twisted her hands together. 'But I don't understand why you were so angry. I know you do not like Fairchilde, but the dance meant nothing. I have never liked him, but I did not know how to refuse him.'

'I don't want him near you. He's dangerous.'

She stared at him, taken aback by the harshness in his voice and face. She pushed a strand of hair away from her face, taking an involuntary step back, suddenly afraid of him, afraid of Fairchilde, and of something she didn't understand—something primitive and completely out of her depth.

He said roughly, 'There's no need to look at me in that fashion. I did not mean to frighten you. But I must know, what did he want from you?'

'Nothing.' He looked as if he could do murder. She

dreaded what would happen if she told him Fairchilde had asked her to be his mistress.

'Are you certain?'

She turned away from him. 'Of course. But this is the most insane thing! Such melodrama is hardly necessary. I could perhaps understand if I was really your fiancée, but even then, such behaviour would not be called for. I am not certain what you think Fairchilde will do.'

'He is completely unscrupulous when it comes to women and to getting what he wants. He will stoop as low as he wishes without regard for anyone.' He took her by the shoulders and turned her to face him, looking into her eyes. 'He indicated once that he had an interest in you. I had thought our announcement would be enough protection. But if it is not, I will not hesitate to call him out. I will protect what is mine.'

'This is ridiculous, my lord. I will not have you fighting a duel because of me. And I am not yours, may I remind you!'

'Yes, you are,' he insisted, his features set in stubborn lines. 'As long as you are engaged to me.'

His dark, handsome face, hovering so close above hers, was rendering her dizzy. Her gaze fell to his firm lips, and for an insane moment she remembered his kiss. What would she do if he kissed her again? She heard his quick intake of breath and knew he was as affected as she. She was jerked out of his grasp, attempting to regain her senses.

'If you call him out, I will break off our agreement. I will not have you putting yourself at such risk, nor do I want such a scandal on my behalf.'

His eyes locked with hers for a moment, then a

slight smile lifted the corners of his mouth. 'I am accounted a deadly shot, my dear. But it is gratifying to know you are concerned for my neck. I was under the impression you often wish me dead.'

'Wish you dead? How ridiculous. I find you extremely provoking, but that does not mean I want you dead.' And especially not now, with him standing there, that half-smile on his face that made her heart beat much faster than it should.

'I am relieved to hear that,' he said softly.

She cast about in her mind for a safer topic. 'Thank you for the roses and the brooch. It is so very beautiful, but it was not necessary for you to go to so much trouble. I assure you, I was not planning to break our agreement over last night.'

'Is that the only reason you thought I sent it? To placate you?' He sounded almost offended.

'No, I…I really did not know what to think.'

'I wanted you to have it. I was waiting for the right time to present it to you. It is a mere trifle, but when I saw it I thought of you. I thought you might like it.'

'Oh. I do. It is very kind of you.' That had not been a particularly safe topic. She was becoming more confused by the minute. Not even John had given her such a beautiful ornament merely because it made him think of her.

'Not at all. I am happy it pleases you.' His gaze studied her face in a way that made her aware that they were quite alone.

Her mind was blank, she could think of nothing to say.

Even more disconcerting, she was completely aware of him, the broad shoulders beneath his dark black coat, the thickness of his hair, his strong masculine features.

'Is something else wrong?' he asked.

'No! I am just rather tired. It is very late.' Why must he stand there watching her with that peculiar look as if he wished to read her soul?

'Is that a hint for me to leave?'

'I suppose you must have other things to do.'

'Such as what?'

'Don't you usually go to a club or…or something?' What else did men do? Visit their mistresses? She could hardly ask him that.

A sardonic smile lifted his lips. 'Since I've met you, my dear, I've spent most evenings attending some damnable function or another. In fact, Caroline informed me tonight that Lady Jersey declares me quite tame.'

'That is hardly my fault. I haven't asked you to attend all of those da—functions! In fact, I would be quite grateful if you would go back to doing whatever it was you did before you met me. Perhaps I could have a bit of peace and some sleep.'

'I believe we've had this conversation before, my dear.' He folded his arms, a sure sign, along with the drawl in his voice, he was going to become even more difficult. 'Spending my evenings at White's will hardly convince my family I hold you in affection.'

She felt unexpectedly hurt that he considered her nothing more than an inconvenience. 'I am beginning to question why this charade is even necessary,' she told him coldly. 'Miss Randall is a most superior young lady in every respect. And you certainly seemed to get along very well with her last night. I have no idea what possible objections you could have towards marrying her.'

If anything, the expression on his face grew even darker. He stalked towards her, causing her to back up against the sofa.

'So you think I should marry Miss Randall, do you?' he snarled. 'I suppose you cherish some hope I'll release you from this arrangement early and you'll be rid of my presence.' His hands came down on each side of her, imprisoning her against the back of the sofa. His dark eyes impaled her. Blood rushed to her head, and she prayed she wouldn't faint. 'I have no interest in Miss Randall. I have no intention of releasing you from our engagement. Furthermore, you will spend as much time in my presence as I deem necessary in order to carry out this betrothal.'

His gaze fell to her lips, his eyes darkening. He brushed a strand away from her face, and she knew he was about to kiss her. She shoved him with all her might. Caught off guard, he staggered backwards.

She beat a hasty retreat behind the sofa, then glared at him. 'Not if you intend to browbeat me in such a revoltingly high-handed fashion, my lord. I pray you will go, or I…I will call my housekeeper. She is very dangerous with a broom!'

He stared at her as if she'd taken leave of her senses. For a moment, she thought he intended to strangle her, but instead he snatched up his gloves and beaver hat.

'A threat to inspire fear in any man's heart,' he drawled. 'You will ride with me tomorrow in the park.'

'I have other things to do.'

'You will be here and ready.'

He turned on his heel and stalked out. She stared at the door, her heart racing furiously. She couldn't remember being so livid in her whole life. Her entire body seethed with anger. She felt like throwing something at the door.

She sank down on the sofa, trying to calm herself. What was wrong with her? What did she care what he thought of her? Why should it matter whether he viewed her as a means to an end or not? He was nothing more than that to her.

As her anger dissipated, she wanted to cry. The carefully constructed wall she'd built around her emotions seemed to be collapsing around her. And the destruction was all due to him.

Chapter Eleven

Michael reined Faro to a walk. He'd hoped a hard ride through Hyde Park would clear his head after last night. Unfortunately, letting his horse run at a full gallop only increased his headache.

No doubt because of his excesses at Fallingham's after leaving Rosalyn last night. He swore. Faro's ears twitched. Somehow she'd managed to pierce through the cool indifference he'd displayed to the world. He couldn't remember the last time he'd felt angry enough with a woman to lose his temper, much less threaten one to do his bidding. Reluctantly, he acknowledged it was because with most women he was quite aware of having the upper hand in the relationship.

But not with Rosalyn. She made it quite clear last night she wanted nothing to do with him, that she only suffered his company because of their bargain. He'd felt that peculiar hurt again when she told him to leave and then he'd blown up at her.

The damnable thing was he wanted her to like him. Several drops of rain fell on his bare head. The grey overcast sky reflected his sour mood. He best get home before he was caught in a downpour.

Watkins opened the door to him. Michael strode past him, only to stop as his butler cleared his throat.

He turned. 'Yes?'

'I have a message for you. I think it might be of a somewhat urgent nature.'

Michael took the note from Watkin's hand. It bore the mark of one of London's jewellers, Compton's, an establishment he occasionally frequented. He had no idea why they would contact him; his bills were always sent to his agent. He perused the contents, then crumbled the note. 'Damn!'

'My lord?'

'Never mind.' He turned and dashed up the staircase to change. Whether Rosalyn liked it or not, she was going to see him now.

But she was not at home. Mrs Harrod, a fount of information where he was concerned, told him she intended to do a bit of shopping and perhaps stop at Hookham's. 'And I will say, my lord, that she appeared a bit overwrought. Great big circles under her eyes as if she hardly slept, poor lamb. I hate to say much, but it's my belief her brother is in a spot of trouble.'

Michael thanked her and decided to head for Compton's in Bond Street. He emerged a half-hour later, after instructing Compton where to send his purchases, more determined than ever to track down Rosalyn. His next stop was at Hookham's library.

She was there, dressed in a grey pelisse, standing in

front of a shelf, thumbing through a book. She did not notice him until he spoke from behind her.

'You're devilish difficult to find, my dear.'

She jumped, the book tumbling from her hands. Her eyes widened in surprise, then a cool expression settled on her features. 'What are you doing here, my lord?'

'I wanted to speak to you.'

'Indeed. I am certain it can wait until later. I am busy now.' She turned back to the shelves in dismissal.

'What I have to say cannot wait until later.'

She gave him an icy glance. 'As far as I am concerned, it can. I am not at your beck and call every hour of the day or night, no matter what you may think.'

He touched her arm. She flinched. 'I don't think you are at all,' he said quietly. 'Will you at least look at me?'

'I am certain I will be forced to do that later.'

'Rosalyn. Look at me.'

She pulled another book from the shelf and determinedly flipped through the pages.

'Then I will be forced to follow you around until you do.'

She finally turned. The expression of martyred resignation on her face was not encouraging. 'What is it you wish, my lord?'

'I wish to talk to you.'

'And I wish to borrow some books. You will have to wait.'

'Very well.' His glance fell to the one at her feet. He bent and retrieved it. 'Is this one you want?' Then he saw the title. He snorted. *'The Libertine?* Is this the sort of thing you read?'

'Give it to me, my lord.' She held out her hand, her face turning pink.

'No.' He thumbed through the volume, a passage catching his eye. ' "…a deadly chill crept through her blood, a universal weakness trembled through her frame, her mouth became parched, now her cheek turned of an ashy paleness…" ' He looked up and grinned. 'Fascinating prose.'

'Please!'

For some reason, the discovery the prim Lady Jeffreys read Gothic novels delighted him. Even more rewarding was watching her cool composure crumble. His ill humour evaporated. He raised a brow. 'And here I thought you read only elevating literature. History, Hannah More's tracts and the like. This is a most enlightening side to your character.'

'Stop it! What if someone hears you?' she said in a fierce whisper. She looked mortified as she glanced around the library.

No one was near them, but he moved closer to her just the same. 'They'll just think I'm reading you love poetry.' He lowered his voice.

She walks in beauty like the night,
Of starry climes…

'Don't! Michael!'

'Ah! You've finally remembered my name!'

'Why are you being so difficult?'

'For the sole purpose of watching you blush.' He

grinned, pleased at the results. She looked utterly dis-
composed. 'Do you want this book?'

'No! I have changed my mind. I don't want any
books.'

'Perhaps another day,' he said kindly. He took her
arm. 'Come with me. I have something for you.' After
setting the book back on the shelf, he propelled her
out of the library.

In front of the library, she stopped and looked up
at him. He saw she looked pale and tired. 'What is it
you want?' she asked.

'I need to talk to you, Rosalyn,' he said quietly. 'We
can't do it here on the street in this rain. I am taking
you home.'

'Home?'

'My home.' He looked around. 'Where is your footman?'

She flushed. 'He has the toothache.'

'And I suppose your abigail is occupied elsewhere.'
He took her arm again and led her down the street.
'You seem to be woefully lacking in servants.'

'I really don't need very many.'

He glanced down at her. 'You should at least have
enough to make your life comfortable.'

'My life is very comfortable,' she said stiffly. 'At
any rate, I cannot afford to keep on a retinue of servants to meet my every whim.'

Unlike himself. His father was one of the wealthiest
men in England. He'd never had to worry about the
lack of money for servants or anything else he'd desired. He had no idea what it would be like to worry
about money.

But one thing did puzzle him. They arrived at his

carriage and he helped her in. After instructing the coachman, he settled in across from her. 'Why are you not staying with your grandmother, Rosalyn?'

She looked out the window for a moment and then turned to look at him. 'Because then my life would not be my own. I want to live by myself and come and go as I please. I don't want to be beholden to anyone.'

Her words surprised him. Not only were they coming from a woman, which was extraordinary enough in his experience, but that they so much reflected his own philosophy. He had spent most of the last ten years avoiding any sort of entanglement that might endanger his independence. His position shielded him from ever becoming financially beholden to any man. But what he had avoided was the other kind, the more dangerous sort, the kind that might mean he could no longer call his life his own. An entanglement that would mean his life was intricately tied to another's.

He looked at the woman across from him. Whether he wanted it or not, her life had become intertwined with his. And he had no idea how to stop it. Worse yet, he wasn't certain he wanted to.

Rosalyn had no idea why she was sitting in Michael's carriage, allowing him to take her to his house without protest. She must be more tired than she realised. Perhaps if he hadn't been so...so nice, she would have worked up the energy to argue with him.

Nice? It was hardly a word she would associate with the arrogant Lord Stamford, but that was what he had been. His unusually quiet manner had broken down her resistance.

Her gaze fell on him. Not that he hadn't been his usual commanding self. No one would ever think him anything but arrogant with the strong, stubborn line of his jaw and the proud tilt of his head.

The carriage halted in front of his mansion. She shivered a little, recalling the only other time she'd been here. If she had known then how bound up in her life the Marquis of Stamford would become, would she have ever come? She had no answer.

The footman had flung open the doors. Michael helped her out, and then took her arm. He hurried her through the rain and up the steps. His butler opened the door.

'Lady Jeffreys will be staying for luncheon,' Michael said.

'Very well, my lord.' He turned to Rosalyn. His stiff face creased in what appeared to be a rare smile. 'May I offer my profound congratulations, Lady Jeffreys, and tell you on behalf of the rest of the staff how pleased we are that you are to be wed to Lord Stamford.'

'Thank you. That is very kind,' Rosalyn replied, taken aback by the sincerity in his eyes. She would have thought, after the first disastrous visit, that he would have quite disapproved of her.

'Come.' Michael allowed her to proceed him up the winding staircase, past numerous portraits of ancestors in wigs, swords, and jewels, to the first floor. Instead of showing her to the drawing room, he took her into the library. She looked around at the dark-panelled room with its shelves of books, instantly liking the warmth of the room. A fire burned in the grate.

'You may wish to remove your bonnet and pelisse,' Michael said. When she hesitated, he added, 'I did not bring you here to rip it up again, if that is what worries you.'

'No, it is just…perhaps I should go home.'

'After we eat. I missed breakfast so I will confess I'm quite ravenous. And I would prefer to eat with company.' A slight smile lifted his mouth. 'I hope you don't plan to suggest I eat at my club.'

She blushed. 'I am sorry. I really did not mean to insult you last night.'

'Have you ever noticed we spend an inordinate amount of time apologising to each other?' he asked.

He was definitely in a most peculiar mood. Neither angry, nor teasing, he seemed to actually want to talk to her.

'I suppose it is because we argue so much. I have no idea why.'

'Neither do I.' He watched her while she removed her bonnet and pelisse with shaky fingers and then indicated a wing chair near the fire. 'Come and sit.'

She hesitantly sat down, wondering what he wanted. He took the chair across from her. The warmth of the fire combined with the steady beat of the rain made her feel warm and drowsy. She forced herself to say, 'What is it you wished to speak with me about?'

'This.' He pulled a small box from his waistcoat pocket and rose. He held the box to her. She took it, after glancing up into his now-expressionless face. 'Open it.'

She did, and then her heart stopped. 'Where did you get it?' she whispered.

'The same place where you sold it as well as your other pieces. Compton's.'

She stared down at her beloved locket. 'But…how did you know?'

'Compton sent a note around informing me you had sold some jewellery.'

She looked up at him with a frown. 'He had no business doing so.'

'He correctly thought I should know. Why did you find it necessary to sell your jewellery?'

'I…I have some debts to pay.'

'Whose debts? Yours or your brother's?'

She looked down at her lap. 'I will pay you as soon as I can.'

He made an impatient sound. 'Rosalyn, the money means little to me. Tell me why. Has James been gambling again?'

She took a deep breath. 'It…it is for an old debt. The creditor wishes to be paid. He is making threats.'

'And who is this creditor?' His gaze was suddenly alert. 'Is it Fairchilde?'

She stared at him. 'Yes.'

'Rosalyn, how well do you know him?'

'He came to Meryton once. I only met him again when I came to London.'

'Rosalyn, why did you stand up with him?' he asked, his voice quiet.

She rose, knotting her hands together. 'He said James was not at Newmarket and if I wanted to know where he was, I would stand up with him. He…he said he always sees to it his debtors pay.'

'Is that all he said?'

'Isn't that enough? I have no idea where James is! I don't know what he owes anyone! And I am worried he…he means to harm James!' Her voice broke.

'Rosalyn, he won't harm James.'

'How can you know that? He…he is despicable.'

'Because I won't let him.' He spoke with such calm assurance she believe him. He frowned. 'Why didn't you come to me instead of selling your jewellery?'

'I didn't think it was—'

'My concern.' He took two steps away from her, then turned. 'When will you get it through your head that you are my concern? I am responsible for you until this damn betrothal is over.'

'But I don't want you to be responsible for me. I…I can manage.'

'You are not managing very well, my dear. How much is his debt?'

'Two thousand pounds. Michael, really, there is no need to worry. As soon as I give the money to Fairchilde it will be over.'

'You're not paying Fairchilde, I am.'

'Michael, this isn't necessary.'

'Yes,' he said ruthlessly. 'You're not going near him. And you will tell me if Fairchilde approaches you again for any reason.'

The vehemence in his voice left her speechless.

Two footmen entered the room, one carrying a heavy silver platter. Michael stared at them for a moment as if he had no idea who had invaded the room. He snapped into motion, directing the servant to set the tray on the massive library table. The footmen then set a smaller table in front of the fire, arranging the two wing chairs on either side.

Michael turned to Rosalyn. 'Shall we eat?'

Without looking at him, she took her place.

After the footmen efficiently set out appetising plates of assorted cheeses, cold meats, pickles, bread, fresh peas, and tarts, Michael dismissed both servants. They departed on silent feet, leaving Rosalyn wondering what to say next.

She stole a glance at Michael. He appeared to be contemplating his wine, a shock of dark hair falling over his brow. She swallowed, the cosy atmosphere suddenly too intimate.

He finally looked up at her, his face serious. 'There is one more thing. About Lady Marchant. Despite what you may think, I was not meeting her that night. She was...' A dull red colour rose up his neck.

'Attacking you?'

'In a manner of speaking, I suppose.' If anything he looked even more disconcerted. He looked back down at his wine glass as if desperate to down the contents, then lifted his eyes to hers. 'She is not my mistress.'

'I see.'

'Well?'

'I was sorry I did not stay and offer my assistance.'

He appeared startled. 'Were you?'

'Yes, but you were managing quite well,' she told him reassuringly. 'I imagine it must happen quite often.'

'No,' he said curtly, then scowled.

She could see he was embarrassed. 'I am sorry. I wished to tease you a little.'

A rueful look crept into his eye. He finally gave her

a slight grin. 'The whole evening was a damnable mess.'

'Yes.' His hesitant smile and the lock of hair falling over his forehead made him almost appear vulnerable. She quickly looked away, before she gave in to the urge to smooth the hair from his brow.

'I hope you eat something,' he said. 'My cook will be on pins and needles wondering if the future Marchioness approves of his cooking. He's rather temperamental. I should hate to have him threaten to leave if your plate comes back untouched.'

'I had no idea a future Marchioness had so many responsibilities.'

He grinned at her, his face relaxing. 'Unending, I'm afraid.'

She sighed. 'I fear I'm ill suited to the role. I will most likely do something to disgrace you.' She thought of the accomplished Miss Randall, the epitome of grace and poise, who would make a most admirable Marchioness.

'You are doing splendidly.'

The warmth in his eyes brought a blush to her face. Completely disconcerted, she picked up her fork. 'I...I had better eat, then. I should hate to be responsible for your losing your cook.'

She ate a few bites of chicken and then looked up to find Michael's eyes fastened on her face. 'You may tell me it is none of my business, if you'd like. Why haven't you remarried?'

She started, spilling a drop of her wine. She was silent and then said after a moment, 'I have not thought much about it. I suppose I don't really care to marry again. I still miss John.'

'So you were fortunate to have a love match?'

'Yes,' she said a little sadly, for it had been despite everything. 'I was very much in love with my husband. I had read some of his work; my father very much admired him, but I had never met John until Father invited him for dinner one night. He was visiting a neighbour of ours. He came every day after that and after a fortnight we were engaged.'

'I see. So you do not think you will fall in love again?'

'No. I really don't want to fall in love again.'

He looked at her quizzically. 'Why not? Most people do.'

'It is much too painful to love someone and have them leave you. I will not go through that again. No, I shall never fall in love with anyone,' she said firmly.

He still watched her in a way that made her feel vulnerable. She said lightly, 'Now it is my turn to ask a question. Why are you so reluctant to marry? Surely you will need to some day.'

'So I have been informed.'

.'You have not answered my question.'

'Very well. I'll tell you. I have yet to find a woman I want to marry.'

'But is it so difficult? I am certain you have had many ready to fall at your feet.'

'Yes. But I don't necessarily want someone at my feet.' He smiled slightly. 'I don't have any particular set of qualities. I suppose I have always hoped I would meet someone the way you met Sir John and know I wanted to marry her.'

She eyed him with surprise. She never would have

guessed he was a romantic. 'You want to fall in love,' she said gently.

'I suppose you think that is quite ridiculous?'

'No, it is not. But even love does not ensure happiness. Sometimes two people can love each other and still live as strangers.'

'Is that what happened in your marriage?'

The penetrating look in his eyes scared her. She had never talked about the reality of her marriage with anyone.

She started to deny it, but found she could not lie to him. 'His work was his true passion, and I cannot blame him for that. I knew when I first met John that it meant everything to him. I had never known anyone with such dedication. That was one of the things I admired most about him. But I thought there would be more time for us. I expected too much from him and it made us both miserable. I was not the wife he needed.'

'Perhaps you expected too much from a man such as Sir John, but you can hardly be faulted. I attended one of his lectures once. He was brilliant. But I could see, even in that short time, how single-minded he was in his purpose. It would be difficult for such a man to give much of himself to anyone. Perhaps he was not the husband you needed.'

His words stung. She had told herself that John had been the only man for her, from the first night she saw him, so handsome and fair and cool, sitting across from her at her parents' dining table. She had fallen in love with him then; he resembled her girlish dreams of a romantic knight. All her mother's cautions against marrying a man so much older had gone over her head. And even in their four years of marriage, as she felt her dreams fade away, she had persisted in her belief that any unhappiness she experienced was from her own foolish desires. It had never occurred to her, until now, that she had may have been wrong.

Tears welled up in her eyes. She set her wine glass down and looked away.

'Rosalyn, I am sorry.' His voice was rough.

She stood up, only to find him in front of her.

His arms came around her, pulling her to his chest. She could not help the tears that coursed down her cheeks on to his coat. His comforting hand stroked her hair. She struggled to gain control of her emotions before she made a complete cake of herself. But it was difficult to pull away from the safe haven of his embrace. No one had held her in such security for years.

But her need for comfort was rapidly overpowered by her awareness of him. His scent was clean and masculine. The strong beat of his heart sounded in her ear. The feel of his hard, muscled body against hers was causing a warm languid sensation in the pit of her being. She pulled abruptly away from him.

'You must think I am a veritable watering-pot,' she said. 'I...I hate to cry. It is just with...James...I am so worried...and Fairchilde...and...' She swiped futilely at her eyes.

He lifted her chin and wiped her eyes with a handkerchief he produced from his pocket. 'Don't worry so much. I'll find James for you. And you'll both be safe from Fairchilde, I promise you.'

'Oh, Michael...' Tears sprang to her eyes again.

'Don't cry,' he said roughly.

'No.' She pulled away, dabbing at her eyes with the handkerchief he pressed into her hands. 'I am fine.'

Trying to clear her head, Rosalyn glance up at the clock on the mantelpiece.

'Oh, no! I had no idea of the time!'

'Is there a problem? You don't turn into a pumpkin or some such thing, do you?'

'That was only the coach,' she said distractedly. She stood up. 'I have been with you over two hours.'

'I see. You are limited as to the amount of time you can spend in my company. An hour at the most?' He watched her with a careful expression.

'It is not that. I do not think it is very proper of me, and we are here alone. Not that you…' She stumbled to a halt, not certain what to say.

His face relaxed. 'Very well. Although our betrothal and your widowhood allows us to stretch the bounds of propriety.' He set his wineglass on the table near the fire. 'I'll call for the carriage and escort you home.'

'That is not necessary.' She wasn't certain if she wanted to be shut up with him in a carriage, even for only a short distance. Her emotions were too close to the surface, too connected to him.

'I want to do it.'

He helped her on with her pelisse and then picked up the box with her locket. 'By the way, I'll return the rest of your jewellery to you.'

She made a helpless gesture. 'Thank you. I…I will pay you. I still have the money. Of course, I must give it to you for Fairchilde.' But then she would still owe him. Perhaps she could get another advance on her allowance.

'I don't want your money,' he said coolly.

'But…'

He shot her a quelling look. 'The subject is beginning to bore me, my dear.'

They rode to her home in silence. The rain had not abated, if anything it was worse. He hurried her up the steps. Mrs Harrod opened the door, and Michael followed Rosalyn into the hallway.

She looked at him uncertainly. 'I don't suppose we are going to ride in the park today?'

His mouth quirked. 'I'm not so much of a taskmaster I'd force you ride in a flood. Will you be at Lady Lavenham's tonight?'

'Yes. With my grandmother.'

'If we are seen there engaged in amicable conversation, all rumours of a quarrel should be put to rest. However, I hope if you change your mind, you'll let me know before I show up. I have no desire to listen to her daughters mutilate various pieces of music for a lost cause.'

'Michael! What a dreadful thing to say!'

He grinned, unabashed. 'But true. You'll see for yourself.' He took her hand, raising it to his lips. 'Until tonight, Rosalyn.'

A shock ran through her at the light pressure. She managed to smile. 'Thank you for the luncheon, and for everything else.'

'Of course.' He stared down at her, looking rather hesitant. 'Caroline is having a houseparty over the weekend. She said she will send you an invitation. Will you come?'

'I…I had planned to. I received the invitation today.'

He gave her a brief smile. 'Good.' He departed.

Rosalyn went to her bedchamber, and sat down on her bed. She lifted the locket from its box, staring down at the beloved, familiar piece. Instead of thinking of her mother every time she saw it, she would now think of him.

Chapter Twelve

Rosalyn peered out the window as the coach rounded the final bend of the lane that led to Longburne Hall. She fought back the bout of nervousness assailing her at the first glimpse of Lord Hartman's primary seat. Certainly it was a lovely house. Built of mellow red brick, it sat in the midst of a large park as if growing there. Clumps of trees surrounded the park. The green, rolling hills in the distance made her think of the peaceful countryside around Meryton.

She settled back in the coach. For once in this betrothal she wished her grandmother was close by. But no, Lady Carlyn had declined the invitation, saying she was certain Rosalyn would do well to have a little time alone with Michael's family. 'After all, they will be your family, dear. I won't always be around to guide you.' Apparently she decided Rosalyn was unlikely to bolt surrounded by his family.

Perhaps she could avoid spending too much time alone with him. After that day in his home, where she had made a fool of herself by crying all over his coat, and forcing him to act as her knight-errant, she had tried to conduct herself with as much dignity as possible. Unfortunately, his very nearness made her shaky as if she was coming down with some illness. But perhaps he would spend most of his time shooting and riding and staying up all night playing cards as men usually did at house parties.

'How pretty it is,' Helena Randall said, breaking into her thoughts. Helena, Rosalyn, and Caroline had shared a coach on the three-hour trip from town. 'I do look forward to leaving London for a few days. 'Twas very kind of you to invite me.'

'I thought you might like a respite from all your suitors. However, I fear I could not exclude all of them,' Caroline said with a wan smile. She had grown increasingly pale as the journey progressed and spoken less and less. Rosalyn worried she had been taken ill, but Caroline insisted she was fine.

Helena sighed. 'I must admit I never knew a London Season could be so tedious. I sometimes think I will say something quite…quite rude if I hear one more compliment on my violet blue eyes! I wish for once to have a sensible conversation!'

The coach entered the carriage sweep, hooves clattering on the paving stones. Liveried footmen sprung out of nowhere to fling the doors open, then helped the three ladies descend to the walk in front of the house. Rosalyn paused and stared up at the house. Four shallow steps led to a terrace in front of the long windows.

Rosalyn followed the others up the steps, feeling hot and sticky in her carriage dress, and waited by one of the columns flanking the entrance as the other carriages arrived. One carried Lady Spence, Elizabeth

Markham and her mother, and Miss Randall's nearly deaf great-aunt. The other chaise carried Caroline's sister-in-law, her husband and an enormous number of trunks and bandboxes.

The other men had decided to ride and now stood by their heated mounts. The riders fared no better: beads of perspiration covered their foreheads, and the fair Lord Brighton's face had turned an alarming red. Charles was mopping his brow with a handkerchief. Only Michael appeared comfortable. Some time during the trip he had removed his riding coat. Rosalyn watched him retrieve it from Lady Spence and shrugged himself into it. He handed his big bay over to a groom and headed for the house.

Rosalyn turned, and hurried through the portico, wanting to avoid him. Ever since that afternoon with him, his very nearness made her edgy.

Caroline appeared next to her. 'Rosalyn, are you well? You looked rather odd for a moment.'

'I feel very well. It was nothing at all.' She looked at Caroline's pale face. 'But I fear you are the one who is ill. You were so quiet on the journey. Are you certain nothing is wrong?'

Caroline gave a little laugh. 'Oh, no. It is just...' She took Rosalyn's arm. 'I am certain I will be better now that we are here.'

'Perhaps you should rest for a bit.'

'You are sweet to worry. It is nothing at all.'

'Rosalyn is right. You should go to your chamber,' Lady Spence interrupted. 'I will take care of your guests.'

Caroline turned to Rosalyn. 'Will you come with me?'

'Of course.'

They stepped around Caroline's sister-in law, Lady Cummings, who was engaged in a heated discussion with the housekeeper.

She followed Caroline up the curved staircase, with its elaborate wrought-iron railing, to the first floor and then down a long corridor. Caroline halted in front of one of the doors. 'I must show you your room.'

'I think we should go to your room first.'

'I am feeling much better. Come and see.'

Rosalyn stepped inside the room. 'How lovely!' The panelled walls were a soft shade of apricot. A light breeze fluttered the muslin curtains and through them, she caught a glimpse of blue sky and green hills.

'I instantly thought of this room for you. It reminds me of you. It will be yours until you marry, and then I imagine Michael will want you next to him.'

Rosalyn could not control the blush that stained her face. Whatever ailed her? One would think she were a young virginal miss who coloured at the mere mention of the marriage bed, not a widow. Besides, she was not even planning to marry Michael.

Unfortunately, Caroline never missed a thing, particularly when it came to romance. She hugged Rosalyn and laughed. 'You are still so shy when it comes to my brother! It is delightful and one of the reasons I like you so well! How refreshing for all of us after all the women who have thrown themselves at him.'

She plopped down on the damask bedcover and patted the place beside her. Rosalyn sat.

The sparkle had returned to Caroline's eyes. 'And I never thought to see him in love! It has quite changed him. He actually seems quite human now! I sometime tease him about being in love and he turns red.'

'Oh, dear,' Rosalyn said

'Oh, no! It is true.' She gave Rosalyn another smile. 'And I have something else I wanted to tell you. Only Aunt Margaret knows and Giles.' A slight blush stained her cheeks. 'I…I am increasing.'

'Oh, Caroline! How wonderful!' This time, Rosalyn hugged her and then released her, catching Caroline's hands. 'No wonder you looked so awful in the coach. That must have been dreadful with all the jostling!'

'Well, yes. At least I didn't cast up my accounts.'

Rosalyn laughed. 'Very true. But I do think you should rest.'

Caroline rose from the bed. 'And so should you. After that, we will have luncheon. You would think I wouldn't want to eat, but sometimes I feel so ravenous!' She gave Rosalyn a fond smile. 'I will send my maid to help you undress.'

After Caroline departed, Rosalyn sat back on the bed. Oh, why must his family be so delighted with her? And they were so kind, so pleased she was to be part of their family. Rosalyn had always wanted a sister to confide in and love, and she could think of no one she would rather have than Caroline.

Why couldn't Michael remain the cynical, uncaring lord, pursuing other women and neglecting his fiancée? Then it would appear she had a valid reason for jilting him. They would undoubtedly think her the most callous woman alive when she broke off the engagement, particularly if he still maintained this pretence of caring for her.

She never considered it might not be a pretence
at all.

The soft voice of the maid roused Rosalyn from a
drugged sleep.

'My lady? Lady Hartman wishes me to inform you
that luncheon is being served on the lawn. Perhaps this
dress would be suitable?'

It took a minute for Rosalyn's groggy mind to reg-
ister the gown of cream muslin sprinkled with small
dark green flowers the maid held up for her inspection.

'That will be fine.' Rosalyn sat up, trying to clear
her head. 'How long have I been asleep?'

'Not more than three-quarters of an hour, my lady.'

It felt like much longer, but the sun had not moved
from when she first shut her eyes. She heaved herself
up from the bed, dressed only in her shift and petticoat.

The little abigail, who could not have been more
than eighteen, made short work of tying the ribbons
of her gown, expertly brushing tangled locks, and pulling Rosalyn's hair into a high knot at the back of her
head. She stepped back, pronounced Rosalyn lovely
and then departed in a great hurry.

Rosalyn located her gloves and a flat straw hat she
was particularly fond of. Her belongings had been unpacked and hung neatly in the mahogany wardrobe.
She found it rather unnerving to think she could sleep
so soundly while someone unpacked her belongings
without arousing her.

She stepped out into the hallway and made her way
down the staircase. A footman sprang forward as she
reached the grand entry hall. She followed him

through the large drawing room and out the French doors to the terrace. Laughter and talk drifted up from below. The rolling expanse of lawn stretched out before them, gently rising to a knoll where Rosalyn caught a glimpse of a summer house in the shape of a classical temple among the trees. A small lake lay beyond that.

She crossed the lawn to join the others underneath the trees. Servants were still bringing out food. Long tables groaned with mounds of chicken, fresh peas, baskets of fresh fruit, strawberries with fresh cream, luscious peach tarts.

Several people she did not recognise had joined the group from London. Rosalyn spotted Michael standing with Charles and Giles. He must have been watching for her as he immediately excused himself from the group.

'Caroline says you have been resting. Are you not well?' Michael said, as he reached her side.

'There really is nothing wrong. Only a little tired, that is all.' Her pulse fluttered at the concern in his voice.

'Perhaps you should still be resting.'

She laughed a little shakily as she glanced up into his face. 'It is hardly that serious. There is nothing wrong with me.'

'I am glad. I worried the heat affected you. Those coaches can be like riding in an oven. What would you like to eat? I shall fetch you a plate.'

'A plate? I don't know. Anything, I suppose.'

He smiled down at her, his face relaxed and teasing. 'Then you're at my mercy, my lady. You may find us a place to sit.'

Small tables and chairs had been set up under the trees. Blankets were scattered about the grass for those who wanted to sit on the ground. Rosalyn chose one of the blankets spread under a towering oak and carefully seated herself on it, arranging her skirts properly over her knees.

Glancing up, she saw Helena stood nearby with a rather uncertain expression on her face. 'Would you care to sit with us, Helena?' Rosalyn asked.

'Thank you.' Helena sank gracefully down beside her. Her simple dress of white muslin emphasised her serene beauty. She smiled at Rosalyn.

'Miss Randall!' Lord Brighton, a thin young man with a carefully cultivated air of Byronic tragedy, hovered over them. He carried two plates of food. 'Are you certain you should be sitting on the ground? I should hate to have you catch a chill. Young ladies with their delicate constitutions cannot be too careful. It would be especially tragic if the fairest flower of the season should lose its bloom.'

'I never catch chills,' Helena replied in a voice that was decidedly peevish for such a soft-spoken young lady. Then an arrested expression appeared in her eyes. 'Oliver?'

A young man in a bottle-green coat and buckskin breeches turned at her voice. 'Helena, what are you doing here?'

'I have been invited by Lady Hartman for a few days.' Rosalyn was amazed to see a blush rise in her cheeks. 'How did you come to be here?'

'I'm putting up with Richard Blenkham. His estate runs next to this. What luck to see you here! Your sister asked me to look you up when I arrived in London.'

By now Lord Brighton was openly glaring at the interloper. Oliver glanced in his direction and an amused expression crept into his eyes. 'Mind if I join you?'

'That would be very nice,' Helena said. Her eyes lit up with pleasure.

He settled down on her other side. She smiled shyly at Rosalyn. 'Lady Jeffreys, may I present Mr Oliver Redding. He is a neighbour of my grandfather's.'

'I am pleased to meet you,' Rosalyn said. She liked his open, intelligent face. He looked quite sensible.

Lord Brighton was less cordial at the introduction, scarcely bothering to open his mouth. Oliver seemed unconcerned at his rudeness.

Lord Philip joined them, followed by Beth and Charles. The small space on the blanket shrank even more when Michael arrived. He dropped down beside Rosalyn, and she jumped when his leg brushed hers.

'It's just me,' Michael said. He set a plate before her.

'I fear I was daydreaming.'

'How complimentary you are. I was hoping you were eagerly awaiting my arrival, and instead I find you daydreaming away amidst a crowd.' He looked around at the half-dozen people seated on the blanket. 'I see a new suitor has joined the hopeful. Who is he?'

'Michael! Keep your voice down. He is a Mr Redding, a friend of Helena's. His estate runs next to her grandfather's.'

'He's certainly putting Brighton's nose out of joint. Perhaps that will have dampened his tendency to quote poetry. Otherwise, I might be forced to forgo my food.'

Rosalyn stifled a giggle. Lord Brighton's poems were truly dreadful. He subjected them to a reading once, and it had been all Rosalyn could do to keep her countenance.

Michael grinned at her and then lowered his voice. He lightly touched her bare arm, sending shivers down to her fingertips. 'Actually, I had hoped we could dine alone. It has been a long time since we have had a tête-à-tête.'

Heat rose in her face. She kept her eyes fixed on her plate. 'Michael, please, not here!'

'Why not? It's perfectly natural for a man to want to spend a little time alone with his betrothed, don't you think?'

'I don't know. I suppose so,' she replied, uncommonly agitated. He sat so close she could feel his warm breath on her cheek. His muscular thighs were pressed against her legs. It was impossible to move away from him on the crowded blanket. She reached for her cup of lemonade and nearly knocked it over.

Michael grabbed the cup and righted it. 'Are you well, Rosalyn?'

'Oh, of course.' She brushed the hair back from her face giving him a vague smile.

'Is the food not to your liking? You are not eating much. I should hate to have you grow weak from hunger,' he said, his voice overly solicitous.

'I find it quite impossible to eat when someone is staring at me in that way.'

'I am merely concerned for your well-being. You should eat a bite of the chicken, it is quite tender.'

She glared at him. He grinned back and popped a forkful of the meat into his mouth.

Why must he bedevil her in front of everyone? At least no one paid any heed since the rest of the men, except Charles and Giles, were occupied with Helena. She stabbed at a strawberry and missed. It leaped off her plate and landed on Michael's lap.

He plucked it up and stared at the fruit before placing it reverently on his plate. 'Ah, a token of your fond affection. I will cherish it the rest of the day. Shall I carry it in my waistcoat pocket?'

An undignified giggle, bordering on hysteria, escaped her. It was impossible to do a thing with him in this mood. 'You are quite fit for Bedlam, my lord. Please don't carry it in your pocket and ruin your waistcoat.'

'Very well.' He ate the strawberry and then set his plate behind him. 'What a lovely smile you have, Rosalyn. It lights up your entire countenance.'

'There is no need to offer me Spanish coin, my lord.' Nor to fix such caressing dark eyes on her face.

'I would never pay you idle compliments, Rosalyn.'

She dropped her eyes and stared fixedly at her half-eaten lunch. Perhaps she was unwell. Uneven pulses, trembling hands, and dizziness certainly could be signs of illness.

Fortunately for her peace of mind, Lord Hartman strolled by to announce some of the gentlemen wanted to get up an informal game of cricket. Michael rose to join them.

The ladies drifted out to watch from the side, parasols raised against the afternoon sun. The day was growing warmer by the minute. The men formed up teams and soon most of them had removed their coats, and several of the more daring their waistcoats.

Watching the game begin, Rosalyn could quite understand why men running about in nothing but breeches and shirts might prove unsettling to female sensibility. She could not keep her eyes off Michael. He was dressed most improperly, and she was fascinated. In addition to discarding his coat and waistcoat, he'd removed his cravat. Muscles as lean as a cat's rippled beneath the thin cambric of his shirt. Tight buckram breeches displayed the contours of his legs and thighs to perfection. Every movement was graceful and effortless. Even the sight of black hair curling over his white shirt in pleasing contrast was most engrossing.

She forced her eyes away, scandalised by her thoughts. Ladies did not stare at a gentlemen's physique in such an assessing and appreciative manner. The hot sun was undoubtedly affecting her reason.

Caroline came up beside her, fresh and pretty in jonquil and cream-striped muslin. She grimaced. 'This will occupy them for hours. It is too hot to stand here watching them tear up the lawn. Shall we go down to the lake? It is much cooler.'

Several of the other ladies agreed. The chattering group made their way to the small lake Rosalyn had glimpsed from the house.

The temperature seemed to drop by several degrees when they reached the water. The soft green lawn sloped down to the edge and tall trees provided welcome shade. A pair of swans drifted in lazy, graceful circles.

Caroline sat down and pulled off her slippers, stockings and gloves. 'I am going wading. Would anyone like to join me?'

Lady Cummings, a plump matron of some thirty-odd years, frowned in disapproval. 'Really, Caroline! What an improper idea and most vulgar!'

'I do it all the time. Giles does not mind. Beth, Rosalyn, want to come?'

'I don't know.' Rosalyn hesitated, but the thought of dipping her bare feet in cool water was tempting.

'Yes, I will go,' she decided. She hadn't done this for years, not since her marriage. John would not have approved. She immediately felt ashamed of her disloyal thought.

Three of the other ladies also declared cooling their toes in the water was a splendid idea. Rosalyn spotted Helena standing a little way off from the others. 'Would you like to join us?'

Helena smiled. 'No, thank you. I believe I will take a walk.' She wandered off towards a wooded grove near the lake.

Rosalyn hoped nothing was wrong, but Helena seemed contented. In fact, she had appeared quite happy since Mr Redding's arrival.

She sat down and removed her slippers and stockings. The grass tickled her toes, reminding her of the sense of freedom she experienced as a girl when she would daringly go barefooted. She pulled off her gloves and then started down towards the water.

Beth stood in the water, laughing. Caroline caught Rosalyn's hand and they gingerly stepped into the cool water, giggling like a pair of schoolgirls.

'Ooh! It is so cold!' Caroline exclaimed.

Rosalyn lifted the hem of her skirt which already

dripped with water. 'Of course, I would wet this the very first thing!'

Caroline took another step forward. 'I used to love to do this.' Then she slipped.

Rosalyn grabbed her, steadying her small frame. 'Caroline! Please be careful!'

'I will. Oh, no!' Caroline cried. Her bonnet had slipped from her head into the water. 'Giles will scold me terribly!'

'Oh, Caroline!' Beth exclaimed. 'It is your new bonnet!'

Rosalyn dropped Caroline's hand and tried to snatch it. Her hand missed and hit the water, making small waves. The bonnet bobbed gently out of reach, its green ribbons trailing behind.

'Oh, dear,' Rosalyn said.

'Tis no matter. I can get it. I've often waded to nearly the middle of the lake.'

Rosalyn prodded Caroline out of the water. 'Caroline, no! You must certainly will not! Giles will really be furious then. Go sit down. I'll fetch it for you.'

'Rosalyn! I don't want you risking your life.'

Rosalyn laughed, suddenly feeling very adventuresome. 'My life? Caroline, I do know how to swim.'

'I can't let you. Michael will be livid!'

That decided her. Rosalyn turned and stepped back into the water. The wayward bonnet rested against the shiny round leaves of a water lily. It did not appear very far away at all. She took a few more steps and then gasped as the gentle slope gave way to a deeper pocket of water. She paused and hitched her skirt nearly up to her waist.

'Be careful, Rosalyn. It gets deep!' Caroline's voice held worry.

By the time she grabbed the bonnet, the water had reached her thighs. Thank goodness the bonnet appeared undamaged except for the edges where it rested in the water.

Squeals of feminine laughter and the deeper timbre of masculine voices reached her ears. She stopped and turned to look. The men must have finished their game for they now gathered around the lake edge. Why of all times, must they show up? She undoubtedly looked like a complete hoyden.

Water soaked her skirt and the bottom of her undergarments. Damp patches spotted her bodice. Her hair, having escaped from its pins, now hung about her shoulders in wanton disarray.

The trip back seemed to take forever. Rosalyn feared she had veered off course for she kept hitting pockets of deeper water. She could hear Caroline shouting something but could not make out the words. Her tender feet, accustomed to shoes and ball-room floors, felt bruised from the rocky bed. Twice, she nearly lost her balance on moss-covered rocks.

She almost reached safety when her big toe hit the edge of a large jagged rock. She squeaked and pitched forward.

Chapter Thirteen

Strong arms encircled her, breaking her fall, and then she felt herself being pulled up against a very familiar, masculine chest. She gasped.

'What the devil are you doing? Are you trying to drown yourself?' Michael demanded.

'I can swim. There is no need to clutch me like that,' she replied, attempting to push her hair from her face. She jerked out of his grasp. Thankfully, she still held Caroline's bonnet.

He glowered down at her. 'What are you doing so far out in the water? You were nearly in over your head.'

'I wanted to fetch Caroline's hat. Besides, the water was only up to my knees.'

'I see. That does make a difference, then. I hardly think Caroline would want you risking your life to get her bonnet.'

'Risking my life?' He was as absurd as Caroline. She stifled a giggle. 'How melodramatic! I can swim in much deeper water. I only wanted to retrieve Caroline's hat before it was ruined.'

'A gardener could have fetched it. I suppose this was one of Caroline's ideas, to engage in such improper behaviour.'

She stared at him, astounded. 'Improper behaviour, my lord? Pray, what exactly do you mean by that?'

He folded his arms across his chest, looking very much like her father when he had been about to deliver a resounding scold. 'You have no stockings or shoes on. You have discarded your hat and gloves. You are not properly dressed.'

She didn't know whether to laugh or hit him. It crossed her mind they must look like perfect cakes standing in the lake arguing, but she was too irate to care. 'Really? You are not properly dressed yourself.'

'It is different.'

'I see. Men are allowed to go about half-undressed, but women cannot remove their hats without being accused of impropriety.'

'I am hardly half-undressed, my dear.'

She coolly appraised him, letting her eyes travel from the damp shirt clinging to his chest down to the point where his ankles disappeared into the lake.

'Indeed? You have removed your coat, your waistcoat, your stock and I cannot see that you have any shoes or…'

'That is enough, Rosalyn. I am carrying you back to the house. You cannot go about with your dress clinging to you in that scandalous fashion.'

'I believe some ladies purposely dampen their dresses for that very purpose.'

'Not with muddy water. And that's hardly the style I wish my fiancée to adopt.'

His tone was so pompous she giggled. His brows

drew together most ominously. He caught her wrist, yanking her towards him. She shoved him away and then watched, horrified, as he fell backward and landed squarely in the shallow water. The expression on his face caused her to fear for her life.

She gathered up her skirts in one hand and waddled out of the shallow water faster than she imagined she could move. The entire company cheered and clapped. She wanted to dive back into the lake. Except Michael was there.

'Splendid!' cried Caroline, running towards her. 'I have always wanted to do that!'

'Better not give the other ladies any ideas,' exclaimed Charles who stood near by, watching the proceedings with a huge grin.

His fiancée cast him a sweet smile. 'Now I know how to keep you in line—I'll keep a jug of water on hand.'

Caroline caught her arm, mixed laughter and consternation written on her face. 'Oh, Rosalyn! Are you quite all right? I fear this was too much trouble for you.'

'Not at all.' She thrust the bonnet into Caroline's hand. 'I think I shall go back to the house now. If I don't show up for dinner, you will most likely find my body in the woods.'

Rosalyn could hear the men teasing Michael. She had best escape now. Completely forgetting her shoes, stockings and straw hat, she nearly ran across the lawn in the direction of the house. No footsteps sounded behind her. Not that she could have heard them anyway over her pounding heart and laboured breathing.

But what would she do when she reached the

house? How to explain why she was alone, without her shoes, hat and gloves, and soaking wet? Her footsteps slowed to a walk. She gazed down at her ruined gown and flushed. No wonder Michael called her improper. The damp muslin revealed every curve. Mud splattered her arms. Her bare toes were every bit as dirty and now had pieces of grass clinging to them.

She limped towards a clump of trees edging the lawn. Her tender feet were bruised from the stones in the lake bottom. Her toe hurt. She leaned against an oak, thankful for its cool shade and closed her eyes in relief, her breath coming in short, shallow gasps. It was all she could do to keep from sinking down on the ground beneath the tree. Grass stains would only compound the damage.

Her relief was short-lived.

'Rosalyn!'

Her eyes flew open. Michael stood near the tree, barefooted, his breeches still wet from the lake, his damp shirt clinging to his chest. Droplets of water dripped from his dark hair. He looked wholly masculine and completely dangerous.

Rosalyn snatched up a branch and clutched it protectively across her chest. 'Don't come near me!'

He laughed and held up his hands. 'Put down your arms. What do you think I am planning to do to you?'

'Strangle me, perhaps. Or drown me.' She eyed him warily.

He came a few steps closer. His eyes danced. 'No, no. Have no fear, you are more valuable to me alive. I would hate to go to this much trouble for another fiancée. Shall we call a truce? I will promise not to harm you if you promise not to hit me with that stick—or push me in the next body of water we come across.'

Rosalyn dropped the branch, her heart thudding as he approached. That devilish glint in his dark eyes was much more worrisome than his anger. He stopped in front of her.

'I think we both need to go up to the house. I don't want you to catch your death from a chill.' He moved closer. She attempted to back around the tree only to find his two hands pressed against the tree on either side of her shoulders, effectively imprisoning her.

'It is far too warm for that,' she said, her heart pounding again. 'Michael, please let me go.'

'I think I should extract a price for your shoving me in the lake.' His eyes strayed to her lips. His voice was low and seductive. 'What do you think?'

'I think you deserved it…I mean being shoved. You were being most objectionable.'

His hand cupped her chin. 'Are you certain?'

She slapped his hand down. 'Stop it, Michael! You are being absurd. I am not going to flirt with you! It is not part of our bargain.'

He stepped away. 'Ah, yes. The bargain. I had almost forgotten. Let me see if I recall your terms. I am not to flirt with you. We are to address each other by our titles in private. And of course, I am never to think of kissing you.'

Her breathing returned to normal. 'No, most certainly not. I am not one of your women, my lord.'

'My women? How many women do you think I have, Rosalyn?' A lazy smile played around his mouth but his eyes held a dangerous glint. He leaned against a tree.

'I…I have no idea. It is none of my business.'

'None of your business? You do not care whether the man to whom you are betrothed keeps a mistress? It does not matter to you at all?'

She backed away. 'Since we are not really engaged I cannot object…that is, I have no claim on you, no claim over what you do.' Apparently that was not the right thing to say for his brows knit together alarmingly.

He folded his arms across his chest. 'We are betrothed, my dear. You do have a claim on me. But for the moment, let us assume you are to be married to a man you loved. Would you care if he had a lady under his protection?'

'Yes, of course I would,' she whispered. 'I would not like it at all.'

'I did not think so.' He shrugged. 'For all it matters to you, I would not insult you by keeping a mistress. Nor, if we were married, would I be unfaithful to you.'

It was the careful indifference in his voice that told her she had somehow hurt him. Without thinking, she moved to his side, touching his hand. He stared at her in shocked surprise.

'Michael, I am sorry. I did not mean to insult you. It is only that everything has become so very complicated. I…I hardly know what we are to be any more.' She feared her words made no sense. 'But thank you for telling me this. I feel very honoured that you would think of me in such a way.'

He dropped her hand as if it burned him.

'Michael? Is something wrong?'

'No.' He ran a distracted hand through his hair, mussing his locks further. 'You are right. This whole bargain has become incredibly complicated. Much more so than you realise, my dear.'

He suddenly seemed to recover himself. 'But I must take you back to the house. You need dry clothing before you catch a chill.'

'I don't think that is likely. The day is so warm that my dress is nearly dry now.'

He held out his hand, and she hesitated, then placed hers within his firm clasp. She winced at the first step. He instantly stopped.

'What is wrong? Are you hurt?'

'No, not really. My feet are a little sore,' she replied and then blushed as his gaze fell on her bare toes peeping from under the crinkled, dirty hem.

'No wonder. That lake bottom is enough to cripple anyone.' Before she knew what he was about, he had swung her up in his arms.

'Michael! Put me down. I can walk!'

'Yes, but I'm afraid if I let you walk now you won't be walking for the next week. No arguments, Rosalyn. I am carrying you to your room.' His mouth quirked at her expression. 'I won't drop you if that is what concerns you.'

That was her last fear. Cradling her against his chest, he headed towards the house. She had never been carried in a man's arms before. His heart beat strongly under her ear, his masculine scent enveloped her. The fine linen of his shirt caressed her cheek. He had rolled up his sleeves; the bare skin of his arms was warm against her own. She felt completely helpless and very, very vulnerable.

She made one last feeble effort to escape him. 'I

am getting mud all over your shirt. You had best let me walk before it is ruined.'

He laughed. 'It was ruined from the dunking you gave me.' He tightened his hold, gazing down at her, his dark eyes lit with a hint of amusement and something else she shied away from naming. 'I like having you in my arms. I have no intention of letting you go.'

Rosalyn flushed and buried her face in his chest. He mounted the terrace steps as if she weighed nothing at all and strode through the drawing room. Lady Spence was just descending the grand staircase when they reached the hallway. She hustled forward, followed by the housekeeper.

'Whatever has happened?' Lady Spence asked. 'Dear child, you are soaked to the skin! And where are your shoes and stockings?'

Rosalyn wanted to disappear. Not only for her missing clothing but because she realised her skirt had become tangled, exposing most of her leg to the knee. 'It is nothing at all and entirely my own doing. I was merely wading in the lake and...'

'And nearly fell in. I am carrying her to her bedchamber.' Michael's arms tightened around her.

'I suppose wading was one of Caroline's ideas,' Lady Spence said resignedly. 'I will send a maid to help you change. I shall also have her draw a bath for you.'

'No, I...'

Michael frowned down at her. 'An excellent idea.' He started up the long curved staircase.

The trip to her room lasted an age. He finally put her down inside the door. She caught a glimpse of herself in the looking glass over the chest and was dismayed at the sight. Her wavy dark hair hung past her shoulders in wanton disarray. A small streak of mud marred her right cheek.

'Oh, dear. I look so disreputable.'

Michael stepped around so he was facing her. He brushed her hair back from her face with gentle fingers. 'Hardly that. You look utterly charming. I like your hair down about your shoulders in such disarray. You are a very beautiful woman, Rosalyn Jeffreys. Did you know that?'

'No…I scarcely think so. I am really rather ordinary.'

He laughed shortly. 'Hardly that, my dear.' He turned on his heel and quit the room, leaving her staring after him.

Rosalyn stood in front of one of the tall bookshelves in Lord Hartman's library. She had never seen such a magnificent collection of books. After dinner, while the ladies had gathered in the drawing room, Caroline had pulled Rosalyn aside. 'I know you adore reading, for Michael has told me. I must show you Giles's library; it is mine too, of course, but he is the one who is always searching for old books. I would rather read another tale by Maria Edgeworth myself.'

Caroline had shown her to the library and then left, telling Rosalyn to enjoy herself. And Rosalyn had, pulling out old volumes and settling down in the comfortable wing chair near the fire to leaf through the pages.

Her gaze settled on a familiar title, *A Treatise on Rome and the Punic Wars*. The author, Sir John Jeffreys. She pulled the book from the shelf, running her hand over its leather cover. It had been the last book John had completed before his untimely death in a carriage accident. He had worked for months on the manuscript, often forgetting to eat unless she reminded him. Most nights, she went to bed alone, while he stayed up working, sometimes until streaks of morning light crept across the sky. He had promised they would take a trip together, perhaps to Scotland, when he had completed the work. Instead, he had died.

Tears pricked her eyelids. She hugged the book to her chest, not wanting to cry. She had barely been able to cry when he was killed and now she seemed to erupt into tears at the least provocation.

'Rosalyn?'

She stiffened. Oh, no, why must Michael come upon her now? He'd think she did nothing but burst into tears like some wretched heroine in a novel. And he'd probably be nice to her again. The thought made her straighten her shoulders. That was the last thing she wanted. 'What is it, my lord?' she said without looking at him.

'My lord? Are we quarrelling again?' She could almost imagine his sardonically raised eyebrow.

'No.' She turned and gave him a feeble smile. 'Did you want something?'

'Yes, you, my dear.'

'Oh.'

He peered more closely at her. 'Is something wrong?'

'No, of course not.'

His gaze fell to the book in her hand. 'Another torrid tale?'

'Hardly. One of my husband's books.'

'I see.' His face lost all expression. 'I wanted to ask you to walk with me in the garden. But perhaps another time.'

His tone of voice held the same studied indifference it had this afternoon when she'd told him his private life was none of her concern. She couldn't imagine what she'd said now that could possibly insult him. 'Michael? Did you wish to discuss something with me?'

'No.' His voice was clipped. 'I will leave you to your books. I beg your pardon.'

'A walk would be very nice,' she found herself saying against all her better judgement. 'That is, if your offer is still open.'

'Yes.' Some of the tension left his face. He waited while she replaced the book on the shelf. 'Do you need a shawl?' he asked when she joined him.

'No.'

He opened one of the tall French doors leading on to the terrace running the length of the back of the house. A light breeze, sweetly scented from the pots of flowers along the terrace, brushed her cheeks. Instead of taking her arm as a proper gentleman should, he curled his fingers around hers in a firm, warm clasp.

'Where are we going?' she finally asked.

He smiled down at her, the tension gone. 'You'll see.'

'It is rather dark.'

'On the contrary, there is a full moon tonight. Most romantic, don't you think?' He was leading her down the terrace steps.

Romantic? They had no business even mentioning

the word between them. She tried to draw her hand
out of his clasp, but he held firm. To make matters
worse, they encountered Caroline and Giles, standing
at the bottom of the stone steps, locked in a passionate
embrace. At their approach, the couple slowly drew
apart. Caroline's lips curved in a knowing smile when
she spotted her brother, not the least bit disconcerted
to be caught in such an embrace with her husband.

'Are you taking Rosalyn to the maze garden? Don't
keep her away too long, Michael, or I shall send Giles
to rescue her. We don't want the other guests to be
scandalised.'

Lord Hartman let out a low laugh. 'You should first
ask Rosalyn if she wishes to be rescued. She may not.
And anyone who is mad enough to marry into your
family must expect a certain amount of scandal.'

Rosalyn's cheeks flamed. It was obvious Caroline
and Giles thought they were escaping for a bit of dal-
liance. Michael merely laughed in passing. 'Don't
scare her off, Giles. She is too prone to bolt as it is.'

'Michael! Please let go of my hand,' she said as
soon as they were out of earshot.

'No.' His fingers closed more tightly around hers.

'Where are you taking me?' Her voice came out
more desperately than she'd intended. They seemed to
be heading much too far away from the house for comfort.

'Only to see a garden.' His voice held laughter.
'Rosalyn, you need not be afraid. I assure you, I am
not leading you to some secluded spot where I intend
to rob you of your virtue. I do have some scruples.
Particularly where you're concerned.'

She bit her lip, chagrined he could read her so easily.

Michael seemed content to say nothing as they passed through a small rose garden and then through an adjoining flower garden. The moonlight, the scents, the warmth of his hand through her glove, enveloped her in a seductive velvet cloak.

The maze lay beyond the wall of the flower garden. By now only the moon provided the least light. Except for the soft sound of their footsteps on the grass, there was silence. They could be alone on their own private continent.

The twists of the maze only increased her sense of wandering into mysterious, unreal territory. And when they finally came through a wooden gate leading to the interior of the maze, she stopped, transfixed.

The light of the full moon bathed the garden spread before them in a soft magical light, touching the pale-hued flowers with silver fairy dust. Cherubs appeared to cavort among the shrubbery and next to a small shimmering pool. Behind the pool stood a summerhouse, built in the style of a small Grecian temple. Two goddesses in ageless marble robes flanked the entry, half-hidden by a curtain of vines.

Michael broke the silence, dropping her hand. 'Caro calls it her fairy garden. Most of the flowers are white or cream, chosen to reflect the light of the moon. If you will observe, many of the shrubs are grey or silver-leafed.' He touched her arm. 'Come and have a look.'

She followed him along the small grassy path dividing the beds. He paused next to some shrubbery and bent down to touch a tall plant with lacy silver leaves. 'See, here is an artemisia. Next to it grows a white rose. And here is a...'

'Gillyflower, my lord.' Any fear she'd entertained he had seduction on his mind evaporated. She suppressed a giggle.

'Gillyflower. Of course.' He glanced at her face, and his lips twitched. 'Is something amiss, Rosalyn?'

'Oh, no. Nothing at all. Do you always come here to discuss the shrubbery?'

'I've never been here with a woman, so I had no idea what I should discuss, particularly with such a lovely woman as yourself.'

'I find that difficult to believe,' she teased, inexplicably happy to learn he had never brought another woman to this lovely place.

He caught her hand again and drew her towards the temple. Near one of the statues, he stopped and pulled her around to face him. He gazed down at her, the laughter in his face evaporating. 'Of course there are things I would rather discuss. Such as how you resemble a beautiful, untouchable goddess yourself in this white gown. And your eyes; they are so wonderfully expressive, but tonight I believe I could almost see into your soul.' His gentle hands slid up her bare arms, coming to rest featherlight on her upper flesh.

She trembled, mesmerised by his touch. Perhaps she was a goddess, but he was a sorcerer, bewitching her with his hands, his voice, his words. His own eyes were dark and mysterious and wholly seductive.

'What...what else did you wish to discuss? Perhaps we should return to the drawing room.' Her voice was oddly breathless. She shivered, and it was not only from the slight wind that fluttered her gown.

'You're cold. We should sit.' He led her to the temple and then pulled her close down beside him on the stone bench. 'Are you warmer now?' His warm fingers trailed down her arm.

'Michael, did you have something to say to me? Something serious, that is?' she added hastily in an attempt to bring the conversation back to sane, practical matters.

'I cannot remember what it was. Your presence is much too distracting,' he murmured.

'I pray you will not flirt with me, my lord.' She stared straight ahead, hands knotted in her lap. Perhaps if she did not look at him, she wouldn't be so susceptible to his dangerous spell.

He sighed and settled back on the bench. 'Why not? It is a very enjoyable pastime.'

'I hardly consider it a pastime. I fear I do not know how to flirt anyway.'

'It is not such a difficult skill. I should be delighted to instruct you, if you would like. I am considered something of an expert.'

'Thank you, but I must decline your offer. I fear any lessons you give would be far too advanced for me.'

'We can begin with the most simple techniques and then progress to more advanced lessons.'

'Michael!'

'Very well, I won't press you.'

'I think it would be best if I returned to the house.' She leaped up from the bench, intending to put as much distance as possible between them. She was not fast enough. Michael rose in one swift motion, catching her wrists in an iron grasp, and hauled her to his chest.

'Wh-what are you doing?' she gasped.

'Capturing your hands so that you don't hit me.'

'Hit you? Why would I want to hit you?'

'Because I'm going to kiss you. Properly.'

'No, Michael...'

'I've been wanting to do this for a long time,' he said, his voice husky. 'At least here we will not be interrupted. Do you object?'

He didn't wait for her reply. His face hovered over her for the briefest of moments, his eyes holding her captive, and then he lowered his head. His lips descended on hers, and began to move in gentle exploration over her mouth as if sampling its sweetness. He let her imprisoned hands flutter free and pulled her hard against him, moulding her soft curves to his hard frame, sending frightening shivers of desire through her body.

It was nothing like his other kisses. A sensuous languor flowed through her, robbing her of every vestige of willpower. She melted against him. Of their own accord, her arms circled his neck and her hands entwined in his thick, silky hair. Under his seductive pressure, her lips parted, inviting him to more passionate exploration. She felt drugged, light-headed; her senses spun out of control as if she were becoming one with him and one with the magical moonlit night.

So this is what it is like to be kissed by a rake, she thought dazedly. Rather like drinking too much wine.

Michael came to his senses first. Kissing Rosalyn Jeffreys the way he'd wanted was proving to be too heady an experience, even for him. The delicious taste of her lips and her light, feminine scent intoxicated him. Her gentle hands tangled in his hair and the soft curves of her breast against his chest threatened to push him beyond reason. If he didn't stop now, he'd be tempted to progress far beyond mere kisses.

Reluctantly, he broke off the sweet, intimate contact and lifted his head, his eyes searching her face. Her cheeks were flushed with desire; her expressive hazel eyes mirrored the same stunned surprise that he had experienced. With gentle fingers, he reached out and smoothed her tumbled hair from her face. As if jolted out of a trance, she started and pulled away. Her hand flew to her cheek.

'I think I should return to the house now,' she said, her voice shaking. She took two steps back, moving as far from him as possible, stumbling on the shallow step. Then she turned and fled.

A light wind had come up, whipping the skirt of her gown as she dashed away, a sprite in flight. Clouds drifted past the moon, casting the garden into shadow. He started after her, fearing she would lose her way or twist an ankle.

'I had best make certain you return safely. You should not be out here alone,' he said, as he caught up with her. He made no move to touch her.

'Thank you.' She said nothing more and for once in their acquaintance he hadn't a clue to what she was thinking. Her face was nearly as expressionless as the statues in the garden.

They retraced their steps through the dark, silent gardens without speaking. At the retaining wall beneath the terrace, he halted by a fragrant climbing rose.

'Rosalyn. We must talk.'

'Talk?' She stared up at him, her face now filled with confusion.

'Yes, I thought you might wish to take me to task or perhaps slap my face,' he said, wanting to tease the bewilderment from her face.

'No. I don't think so.' He could visibly see her attempting to retain her composure. She added distractedly, 'I have never been kissed by a…a rake before.'

He nearly laughed. 'Haven't you? How did you find the experience?'

'It was rather interesting.'

'Interesting? Merely interesting? I must be losing my technique. Next time I must make sure you find it something besides interesting.'

'I…I don't think there should be a next time. That was not part of our agreement.'

'Agreements can be renegotiated. I would be quite amenable to changing the terms of ours…' he began, but stopped when he saw the panic on her face. He was going too fast for her. He added more gently, 'We can discuss this later.'

She tore away from him. 'No, there is nothing more to say! I do not want to change the terms of our agreement. I pray you will never kiss me again!'

He caught her arm, pulling her around to face him. 'What are you afraid of, Rosalyn? Are you afraid of me? I swear I will not hurt you.'

'Please! Don't touch me. I wish to be alone.' She wrenched herself away from him and flew up the stone steps to the terrace.

Michael watched her retreating form as he leaned against the retaining wall. He ran a distracted hand through his hair. He wanted to go after her; take her in his arms and show her there was nothing to fear, but he knew that would only drive her to further retreat.

Besides, he needed time to sort out his own chaotic thoughts. Since that day in the library, he'd tried to refrain from touching her, but free from the restraints of a London ball room, he'd found it difficult. Carrying her in his arms today had pushed him to his limit. And when he found her in Giles' library, tears in her eyes over her husband's book, he experienced the fierce desire to erase all thoughts of Sir John from her mind.

He nearly groaned aloud. Any hopes he'd had that kissing her would put his curiosity to rest had vanished. Instead, his smouldering desire had burst into flames. He had wanted many women, but never with the same mixture of desire and protective tenderness that Rosalyn aroused in him tonight.

He should have known he was in trouble when he attended balls and routs only to see her, when other women held little attraction for him. When he actually found his role of fiancé a pleasure rather than the painful duty he'd always imagined. And most of all, when he was filled with the murderous desire to put a bullet through Fairchilde for waltzing with her.

He feared he was too far gone to turn back. Offering her *carte blanche* was out of the question; she was not the sort of woman he could unscrupulously take for a mistress.

He supposed there was nothing to do but persuade her to marry him.

The irony of it struck him. Wanting her for his wife was the last thing he'd planned on when he'd forced this damnable bargain on her. But fate had played his own hand against him. Amazing to find he was looking forward to the chains of matrimony, if it meant he were chained to her.

However, one small problem remained—his fiancée would rather go to the devil than wed him. He had felt her sweet response tonight and knew she wasn't as indifferent to him as she wanted to believe. But convincing her of that…that was another matter. He had until September to convince her she did want to marry again. Him.

He moved up the steps and crossed the terrace. Lights blazed from the drawing room. Inside he could see his sister and several guests hovering around a table, undoubtedly engaged in emptying each others' pockets at loo.

He needed to plan his strategy carefully. He'd need to employ all his methods of persuasion to break down her resistance. He only hoped he was up to the task.

He smiled, a smile without humour. Now that he'd finally made up his mind to take a bride, he had no idea if the lady would comply.

Chapter Fourteen

After breakfast the following day, Rosalyn wandered through the gardens near the house, finally making her way to a bench underneath a small vine-covered pergola. She sat down, the air fresh and clean after last night's rainstorm.

In the rational light of day, she blushed to think of her eager response to Michael's kisses. His touch had erased all thoughts of John or, for that matter, anything else. This was dreadful. She felt as if she were losing control not only of her life, but of her carefully protected emotions.

She leaned her head against one of the pillars. Of course he was a flirt and undoubtedly kissed many women, but why would he want to kiss her? She couldn't fathom that a man such as the Marquis of Stamford would find her desirable. But afterwards, when he had lifted his head, all the teasing laughter gone from his face, she saw he'd been as affected as she had. He desired her.

And she desired him. The revelation hit her with shocking force. She closed her eyes. Oh, heavens, how had this ever happened? Somehow her initial dislike had turned into a devastating attraction. Worse, she actually like him, liked his humour, his intelligence, his charm, his unexpected kindness. She couldn't think of a more disastrous thing to have happened. She must not, could not, allow herself to fall in love with him.

A faint rustle made her open her eyes. Michael stood near the entrance to the pergola, handsome and all too masculine in his dark brown coat and breeches. He wore riding boots and in his hand carried a crop. 'Good morning, Rosalyn,' he said.

Her pulse quickened at the lazy, intimate tone of his voice. 'Good morning.'

He moved towards her with leisurely grace. 'I missed you at breakfast. I'm afraid I didn't rise as early as I had intended.'

'None of the men were up, so you are in good company. It makes one wonder what you do all night.'

He grinned. 'Nothing of significance, I'm afraid. Play billiards. Attempt to fleece each other out of our respective fortunes. Argue over the best way to govern the country, accompanied by a half-dozen bottles of brandy, of course.'

'How fascinating.'

'Sarcasm from the sweet Rosalyn Jeffreys? What other surprises do you hold under that innocent exterior?'

'None at all.'

'May I sit?' He indicated the spot next to her on the bench.

She shot up, unnerved by the thought of having him squeeze next to her on the small bench. 'I…I was just about to return to the house. Lady Cummings has asked if I would like to accompany her on a walk.'

'I have other plans for you.'

She stared at him. 'Such as what? Are you not going riding?'

'Yes, but with you. My day is at your disposal. Or rather your day is at mine. We're going on a picnic.'

'A picnic? I haven't heard any plans for a picnic.'

'This will be a private picnic. Just you and me.' His mouth still curved in a half-smile, but his eyes were alert with an expression she could not fathom.

She flushed. 'I really don't think it is such a good idea. And what will the others think if we go off by ourselves?'

His smile was wicked. 'They will think we wish to be private, of course. Put your mind at rest, Caroline thinks it is a splendid idea, as does my aunt. Any other objections?'

Rosalyn could think of at least a half-dozen more. But her mouth had gone dry.

'Did you bring a riding habit?' he asked.

'Yes.'

'Good. I will walk with you to the house so you can change. What sort of mount do you prefer? Caroline has offered you the use of any of her horses.'

She found her tongue. 'But I haven't said I will go with you.'

'But you will.'

'Are you always this certain you'll have your way?'

He tucked her arm through his, then turned his maddening smile on her. 'Yes, most of the time. If I set my mind to something, I generally get what I want.'

They began walking towards the house. 'You must have been a very disagreeable child,' Rosalyn said.

'Not at all. I believe I was considered a very charming child. I learned early there are many ways to achieve an end without throwing a tantrum. Often, a more subtle approach works best.'

She glanced up at his dark handsome face and his laughing eyes with their devastatingly long lashes. She could quite imagine how that worked. She could not keep the tartness from her voice. 'I see. You wind everyone around your finger by charming them into doing what you want.'

'Except for you. I cannot see that I have been able to charm you at all.'

'I believe we agreed you attempt to intimidate me.'

By now, they had reached the steps leading to the terrace outside the drawing room. He halted and looked down at her. 'I fear we are about to quarrel again. I don't wish to argue with you, Rosalyn. Admit you will go with me, or else I will be forced to persuade you by a different means.'

'Will you? And what method is that?'

He pulled her towards him. 'This.' He bent his head. His lips brushed across hers, sending a shiver down her spine. He lifted his head, a slight smile curving his mouth.

She backed away from him, giving a quick nervous glance towards the drawing room windows. 'Michael! Don't! What if someone sees us?'

'Will you agree or not? Otherwise I will be forced to take more drastic measures.'

The glint in his eye told her he was fully capable

of doing so. 'Yes, I will go, but please don't do that again!'

He grinned. 'Then go change and hurry back.'

When she returned, after changing into her bottle-green riding habit, Michael was waiting where she'd left him. Philip stood with him. He looked up as Rosalyn hesitantly descended the steps. 'I'd best be leaving. I am most certainly *de trop.*'

'You would not be,' Rosalyn said, who was experiencing a moment of panic when she saw Michael. 'In fact, if you wished to join us, I am certain there would be no objections.'

'Perhaps not from you, but there most certainly would be from another quarter. No, thank you, I don't want a quarrel forced upon me.'

'Very wise of you,' Michael said drily. He glanced down at Rosalyn, a gleam in his eye that boded no good. 'Come, my love.'

Philip grinned as he started up the terrace steps. 'You'll be fine. Just shove him in a trout stream if he misbehaves.'

Michael and Rosalyn started down the path to the stables. 'There's no need to recruit a chaperon,' Michael said. 'Are you still convinced I mean to seduce you?'

'No, of course not.' She flushed uncomfortably.

'Although I might like to.'

'Michael!'

'You are very seducible, you know.'

She nearly walked into a rhododendron bush. He pulled her away. 'Seducible? Are you implying that I am a woman of loose morals?'

'Not at all. Merely that you are very desirable. It would be quite easy for a man's thoughts to stray when in your company.'

'How ridiculous! I have never had that effect on any man in my life!'

'Not even Sir John?'

'No!' Horrified at speaking of something so intimate, she said, 'Of course, he…he thought I was pretty.'

'That is not the same as desirable.'

'Michael…'

'He was a fool if he didn't find you so,' Michael said ruthlessly. He halted and pulled her around to face him. They stood in the shadow of one of the stable buildings.

She looked up at him. 'I don't wish to discuss my husband or my marriage. John was kind to me, and I…I know he loved me.'

'Of course.' His expression softened, and he traced a gentle thumb down the curve of her cheek to cup her chin. 'But you are more than merely pretty, you are lovely and intelligent and kind, and very, very desirable.'

Oh, no! Why must he do this to her? She nearly closed her eyes, wanting nothing more than to sway towards him, feel his arms close around her. Then sanity returned. 'Shouldn't we be going?'

He dropped his hand. 'Probably.' Then he gave her a half-smile. 'Some day I plan to wipe all practical considerations from your mind.'

'I hope not.' But his words made her pulse race all the same.

The groom had the horses saddled and ready. Next

to Michael's bay gelding stood a smaller chestnut horse. 'Sir Henry's as gentle as a kitten,' the groom informed her as he helped her mount.

'Although I've had some nasty scratches from kittens,' Michael said. They had started across a pasture near the stables.

Rosalyn gave him an exasperated glance as she patted the horse's neck. 'I am certain Sir Henry doesn't scratch. He seems to have a very nice temper.'

Michael merely grinned at her. She smiled back, suddenly happy to be on a horse again, enjoying the smell of the country air after so many weeks in London. The sky was a bright cobalt blue, the trees and grass had the lovely dewy freshness that followed a night's rain. The air smelled clean and pure, the birds twittered in the trees, and a pleasant breeze caressed her cheeks. With a sense of wonder, she realised she felt more at peace than she had for a very long time.

She glanced at Michael and saw he was watching her. 'You look happy,' he said.

'It is a lovely day, don't you think?'

'Yes. I don't believe I've seen you look like that before.'

'Oh.' She coloured, a little embarrassed by his scrutiny. 'Where are we going?'

He slanted a glance at her. 'There's a secluded spot near an old cottage. I thought you might like it.'

'It sounds very nice.' She stole a glance at his strong profile and thought he also looked relaxed, as if the day pleased him.

They rode in a companionable silence. The path wound by the lake and through a stand of trees. At last, they came out of the trees to a clearing where an old two-storey brick house stood. Vines rambled up a side wall and tall rhododendrons surrounded the front door. Michael reined his horse to a halt and waited for Rosalyn to amble up on Sir Henry. 'This is the cottage,' he told her.

'It is not occupied, is it?' she asked.

'No. It once belonged to a Dowager Countess who didn't want to reside very close to her son and daughter-in-law. Caroline sometimes comes here when she wants solitude. And she and Giles often come for a day or two. It's rather sparsely furnished, but the roof is in good repair.'

He dismounted in a graceful motion and then held out his arms to help Rosalyn down. She slid awkwardly off the horse and fell against him. 'I'm sorry,' she gasped, pushing herself away.

'I'm not.'

She heard the teasing in his voice and flushed. 'Where will we eat?'

'There's a spot behind the cottage or we can eat inside. I have a key. Whichever you prefer.'

'Outside. It seems a shame to waste such a lovely day.'

He secured the horses and then took Rosalyn's hand and led her around the side of the cottage. A small overgrown lawn lay behind the building, surrounded by tall bushes and trees. A rustic stone bench sat in one corner. Michael led her to the bench. She sat down and waited, wondering what to do or say next.

'Are you hungry or should we walk first?' he asked.

'I am actually quite hungry. I only had tea for breakfast.'

'Then we'd best eat. I'll retrieve the food.'

Looking around, she saw nothing resembling a basket. 'Where is the food?'

'It should be in the cottage. There's actually a more direct route here, but the longer ride is more enjoyable. I will get it.' He turned and strode toward the cottage. Rosalyn rose and followed him.

He thrust a key into the lock and then swore when the lock refused to budge. The door suddenly gave way. A sheepish look crossed his face. 'It wasn't locked.'

'I hope this doesn't mean our picnic has been stolen,' Rosalyn said.

He looked at her, his mouth curving in a smile. 'We'll just have to find something else to do to keep our mind off food, then.' His glance drifted to her lips. 'I can think of a few things,' he added suggestively.

Rosalyn flushed in spite of herself. Keeping him at bay was going to be difficult if he persisted in those sort of remarks. 'I'm afraid nothing will keep my mind off food when I am hungry.'

'Are you certain?'

'Perhaps we should look for the food, my lord.'

He heaved a mock sigh. 'I can see you're determined to keep me in my place.'

They found the baskets in the small dining room. As Michael had said, the cottage was furnished very plainly, but its simplicity was inviting. It looked cosy and intimate, the sort of place one might go to meet a lover.

Her thoughts made her blush. What was wrong with her? She had never thought in such a manner before meeting him. And after his words near the stable, she'd best keep her thoughts on the practical.

She helped him carry the baskets over his protests that he could do it all. She found a cloth in one of them and spread it out on the ground. After removing her hat, she sat down on the cloth.

Michael joined her, then shrugged out of his coat. He rolled up his sleeves and leaned over one of the baskets to retrieve a dish. His wayward lock of hair fell over his forehead. Rosalyn swallowed at the sight of his bare, sinewy arms and the muscles stretched taut under his shirt. Perhaps a private picnic had not been such a good idea.

He removed another dish before she started out of her trance. She couldn't sit here and gape at him. Cheeks red, she reached into the other basket and pulled out a bottle of wine and two glasses, then plates and silver.

Michael set out the last dish and surveyed the spread before them. 'Good lord! There's enough food to feed Wellington's army.'

She laughed at the expression on his face. 'As long as we don't have to eat it all.'

He uncovered a dish. 'What will you have? There is chicken, ham, cheese and pickle, not to mention a cake and tarts. Shall I serve you?'

'You served me yesterday.' She reached for a plate. 'What would you like?'

He leaned back on one elbow and grinned. 'Anything. I'll let you decide since you made me do so yesterday.'

Perhaps she should have let him serve. He watched her every move as she dished out slices of ham and chicken, chunks of bread, pickles and asparagus. The ordinary act suddenly seemed extraordinarily intimate under his half-closed eyes.

He sat up as she moved towards him. She handed him the plate, her hand brushing his as he took it. She started to yank her hand away, but he caught it, giving her a lazy, heartstopping smile. 'This is very nice, Rosalyn. I like having you wait on me.'

Her startled eyes met his. His smile deepened. 'Last night you looked like a goddess; today you resemble a lovely fairy suddenly captured by a mere mortal.'

'Michael, this is ridiculous! I...I am not a fairy.'

'But you are. Weaving a spell around me.'

'Shouldn't we eat?'

'Only if you promise not to flit away.'

'I have no intention of doing so.'

He slowly released her. 'I hope not.'

She scooted back to her side of the cloth, heart pounding, heat flooding her cheeks. What was he trying to do to her? Certainly he was flirting; there was something more dangerous, more sensuous in his manner than she'd ever noticed before.

She helped herself to the food, wishing he'd pay attention to his plate instead of to her. She sat back, hardly knowing what she'd put on her plate.

She took a few bites. The food was good, and she was hungry. They ate in silence, the sounds of birds and the nearby stream providing a pleasant accompaniment. Finally, Michael reached for the bottle of wine. He opened it, then poured two glasses. He handed her one.

She took it, pleased her hand did not tremble. 'Thank you.'

'Not at all.' He took a sip of his wine, then set the glass down. 'Rosalyn, we need to discuss last night.'

She spilled a drop of wine, her cheeks hot. 'There is nothing to say. I dare say we were both carried away by the garden and the moonlight, that is all.'

'So you think our passionate kiss was the result of smelling the roses or some sort of madness induced by a full moon?'

'Well, yes, something like that. It should never have happened.'

He set his wine glass down and looked at her with a great deal of speculation. 'An interesting theory. And why should it not have happened? Despite your attempts to deny it, there is some attraction between us.'

'We have a bargain, an agreement. We…we can't afford to do that sort of thing.'

'Can't we?'

She made a helpless gesture. 'Michael, please! Why must you be so difficult?'

He suddenly smiled. 'Because you get so delightfully confused.' He rose in an easy movement. 'Shall we walk for a bit?' He held out his hand.

She took it, allowing him to help her to her feet. His abrupt change of subject did nothing to restore her equilibrium. At least he seemed to have decided last night was a mere aberration. Which was exactly how she viewed it.

They left the lawn surrounding the cottage and strolled towards the stream. 'Shall we sit?' he asked, indicating a grassy spot under a tree.

'Perhaps a walk would be better.'

He deposited himself on the grass and leaned back against the tree, legs stretched out before him. 'But I'd rather sit. And I don't want you wandering off by yourself.'

'I have been on my own for some years.' Rosalyn sighed and finally sat beside him, careful to avoid the slightest contact with any part of him. Not that she could keep her eyes from straying to his well-muscled thighs encased in tight buckskin breeches. Or from noticing his strong lean fingers as they plucked a blade of grass. Her whole body tingled with awareness of his masculine presence.

He suddenly turned to look at her. 'So you think our kiss was nothing more than moon madness?'

'I really do not wish to discuss it.'

'But I am curious. Shall we determine if your theory is correct?'

'No. We should not.' Her voice did not sound at all convincing as he moved closer to her. She froze as one arm circled her back. His other hand tilted her chin so he could look into her eyes. His own eyes were warm, a half-smile hovered on his lips.

'If your theory is correct, this should have no effect at all.' He bent his head and kissed her.

She should have struggled, pushed him away as his lips moved over hers. Instead, she sighed and melted into his embrace as if she'd been waiting all day for this very moment. He ran a trail of kisses down her throat, pausing to nibble the pulse at the base of her neck, then lifted his head. 'What is your conclusion?' he asked, his voice husky.

'I...I don't know.' She made a supreme effort to regain control of her traitorous body. 'Our...our agreement.'

'To hell with the damned agreement.'

This time he pulled her hard against him, his mouth crushing hers.

Her arms went around his neck, pulling him closer, knowing now she had wanted this. Her lips parted under his, allowing him entry to explore the warm recesses of her mouth. His hands came up to pull the pins from her hair and her hair tumbled around her shoulders.

He lifted his head for a moment, but only to lower her gently to the ground. He braced himself on his elbows above her and stroked her cheek. 'You are beautiful.'

She closed her eyes, the intensity of his gaze burning through her. He fumbled with the hooks of her bodice and then deftly unbuttoned the shirt she wore beneath her habit, pushing it aside. All rational thought fled when the warmth of his hand caressed her tight, swollen breasts.

His mouth moved leisurely down her neck, leaving a trail of fiery kisses. He moved lower and when his tongue swirled over a peaked nipple, she gasped and arched against him.

His shirt had come loose from his breeches. She slipped her hands beneath it and ran her hands over his smooth, bare skin, revelling in the feel of the hard, taut muscles beneath. Her touch seemed to inflame him more. He groaned and his mouth moved back to possess hers.

Then he pulled up her skirt, his hand coming to stroke the silkily soft skin of her thigh above her stocking. But when his hand moved further to touch the sensitive cleft between her thighs, he suddenly pulled his hand away and rolled off her, pulling her skirt down.

Confused and ashamed by her own behaviour, she lay there, eyes closed until she felt his hand brush her cheek. 'Rosalyn? My sweet, did I hurt you?'

She opened her eyes to find him braced on one elbow, his face hovering over hers. A lock of hair hung over his forehead and his eyes were filled with concern.

'No. Please…move,' she whispered. He did so, leaving her feeling strangely bereft. She sat up, her face suffused with heat, attempting to compose herself.

Her hands trembled as she fumbled with the buttons which refused to cooperate. How could she be so foolish? If he hadn't stopped when he did, she would have let him make love to her. Not only let him, eagerly welcomed him.

Michael leaned over and gently pushed her hands away. 'Allow me.' With deft fingers, he fastened the buttons. She stared down at his dark head, aching with the need to touch him again.

He finished and stood up, and tucked his shirt into his breeches. Then he reached down to pull her to her feet. She could not look at him, afraid to see the look of contempt on his face. She pushed a strand of hair away from her face with fingers that still shook. How was she ever going to pin her hair up? Her hairpins lay scattered on the ground. She bent down to retrieve them, only to find Michael there before her. His hand brushed hers, and she hastily straightened up.

'I had best help pin your hair up, since I was responsible for its destruction,' he said. His voice was matter-of-fact.

She finally glanced at him, stunned by his calm. He sounded as if nothing had happened between them. But then, nothing had. He had made it painfully obvious he did not want her.

'Turn around,' he said.

'Turn around?' His words finally sunk in. 'I…I can manage my hair.'

'Isn't it difficult to do without a maid?' he inquired.

He wanted to discuss the finer points of dressing a lady's hair now?

'Well?' he asked. He seemed to really want to know.

'I suppose to do it properly it can be. However, I have done it before.' She frowned at him, not really wanting to attempt to pin it up with him watching her. It seemed a curiously intimate motion. But she could hardly return to the house with it tumbling past her shoulders. One look at her hair and wrinkled habit and everyone would guess what else they had enjoyed besides the picnic.

She turned her back to him and gathered her hair up, twisting it into a knot away from her neck. The next thing she knew, Michael was behind her.

'Let me help you. You have grass in your hair.' He plucked her hands away, untwisted the knot, then ran his fingers down the length of her hair as if to comb out the tangles. She froze, the feel of his fingers sending a languorous shudder through her being. Good Lord, what was he trying to do to her?

'You have beautiful hair. I noticed that the first time I saw you.'

'Di-did you?'

'Yes.' He lifted her tresses from her neck. 'What do I do next?'

What? 'Um, I…I usually gather it into a knot and then pin it on top of my head.'

'Like this?' She felt him knot her hair, then hold it while he fumbled with the hairpins.

'Yes.' The feel of his hands in her hair was producing the most exquisite sensations. She closed her eyes, praying she wouldn't do something rash such as throw herself at him, begging him to finish what he had interrupted.

He finally dropped his hands away. 'I don't think I am particularly talented at this. It looks rather lopsided. Perhaps I should try again.'

'No!' She nearly leaped around to face him. 'I…I am certain it is fine. And after I put my hat on, no one will even notice.'

'If you are certain.' He eyed her critically.

'Oh, yes. Thank you. I think we should go. Isn't it getting rather late?' She looked up at the sky as a cool breeze brushed her cheek. While they'd been occupied with other activities, heavy grey clouds were darkening the sky. 'I am afraid it might rain.'

'You're undoubtedly right.' He didn't move. 'Do I have grass in my hair?'

'I beg your pardon?'

'I thought you would like to perform the same office for me. Pull out any grass, brush your hands through my locks, remove any evidence of our day's activities from my person.' His mouth quirked.

'No, I…I think we've done enough of that sort of thing for today.'

'Will you at least see if all the grass is gone?'

He was utterly mad. They could stand here until dinner at this rate. She moved closer to him. He did have a piece caught in his thick hair. She reached up to remove it, feeling his breath on her face. He stood perfectly still until she stepped back. 'There. It is gone. Michael, we really must go.'

'Very well.' His voice sounded peculiar again. He retrieved his coat and shrugged himself into it, then in silence they walked back to the cottage, careful to avoid contact with each other.

Chapter Fifteen

To make matters worse, the clouds began to gather; by the time they neared the stables, light raindrops had started to fall.

Michael dismounted first and then went over to help Rosalyn down. He resisted the urge to let his hands linger on her waist, but instead quickly released her. She jerked away as if bitten by his touch.

They hurried back to the house, as the rain began to pour. Michael cursed himself. What in the devil had possessed him to practically seduce Rosalyn under the tree? He'd planned to take her on the damned picnic, talk with her, flirt with her, perhaps steal another kiss, not tumble her on the ground like a wench from a tavern. Then, in his clumsy efforts to help her rearrange her clothing and hair, he'd undoubtedly made a fool of himself.

He stole a glance at her. Her face was pale and quiet, and he had no idea what she was thinking. Her hair was falling out of her hat in a charming but rather untidy disarray. He'd never be hired on as a lady's maid if that was the best he could do.

Caroline was coming down the staircase as they entered the hallway. 'I saw you coming from the drawing-room window,' she said as she reached the bottom step. 'I thought I should warn you. Papa is here!'

'Good God!'

'He arrived only a hour ago. He is most impatient to meet Rosalyn.'

'Oh, no,' Rosalyn said faintly.

Looking over at Rosalyn, Michael saw her face had lost all colour. He touched her arm. 'He won't bite.'

'Really, he will not, Rosalyn,' Caroline said with a quick smile. 'Come, you only need to change and then you'll be quite presentable.' Caroline took her arm. 'I know he will quite adore you as we all do!'

Rosalyn looked stricken. She cast Michael a helpless glance as Caroline led her away. He gave her a reassuring smile.

Then Caroline stopped and turned back to him, her eyes full of mischief. 'I suggest you change also, Michael. You have grass in your hair.'

The Duke was standing near the long French windows in the drawing room when Michael entered. By now, the rain poured down in sheets. His aunt sat on the sofa next to Helena Randall. Beth and Lady Cummings sat together at a table playing cards. They gave him a curious glance when he entered, then turned back to their game.

Eversleigh turned as Michael reached his side. Tall and erect with a harsh, handsome face, he hardly looked his fifty-some years. He was still thin after his illness, but Michael was relieved to see his colour had returned.

'What brings you here, sir?' Michael inquired as he joined his father.

Eversleigh raised a brow. 'A desire to meet your fiancée. Since you do not seem inclined to bring her to Eversleigh, I thought I'd best come here.'

'Are you certain you're fit to travel?'

'I am not quite on my deathbed yet,' he said. 'Where is Lady Jeffreys? I have been assured she does exist, but I've yet to see her for myself.'

'She went to change from her riding habit.' Michael glanced toward the doors. Where the devil was she? Nearly a half-hour had passed since they had arrived at the house. The idiotic notion she decided to escape through a window crossed his mind, then was just as quickly dismissed.

The drawing-room doors opened and, to his infinite relief, Rosalyn appeared with Caroline. Dressed in a simple rose gown, her hair now properly arranged, she looked cool and composed as Caroline brought her forward. Only her hand going to her locket before she swiftly brought it to her side betrayed her inner nervousness.

Michael performed the introductions. Eversleigh took her hand. 'I have looked forward to this moment, Lady Jeffreys.'

'Thank you, your Grace.' Her voice held the faintest tremor but Michael saw she kept her gaze steady.

The Duke released her hand. 'I hope to see you soon at Eversleigh.'

She looked startled. Michael moved closer to her. 'Perhaps I can persuade her to come for a visit.' It might be the perfect place to continue his courtship.

Without too many picnics. The very thought made his mouth go dry.

He jerked his thoughts away from the images and realised his father was speaking. 'A visit is not quite what I meant. I hope to see Lady Jeffreys there on a more permanent basis.' This time Michael started. His father fixed him with a piercing stare. 'As your wife. That is why I am here. I see no reason to delay your marriage any further. When we return to London, we will proceed with the arrangements.'

Michael felt as much as heard Rosalyn's faint gasp. He turned and saw she had gone white. She looked as if she had been sentenced to death.

A cold pit formed in his stomach. It was obvious she had no desire to marry him, not even after their passionate lovemaking earlier. Now with his father's precipitate announcement, he had little time for the courtship he'd planned.

And no matter how much he desired Rosalyn, he had no intention of having his father force her to the altar.

Rosalyn had no idea how she made it through dinner. She sat between Michael and Philip, hardly tasting the food, hardly knowing what she said. She had never been prone to hysterics or swooning, but when Eversleigh announced that plans for their wedding should be made immediately, she had thought she might faint for the first time in her life.

Now she sat in the drawing room, anxiously waiting for the men to finish with their brandy and conversation. She hoped they were not planning to stay up half the night in the dining room. She must speak with Michael.

She rose from the chair, too agitated to sit. Michael had been silent and distracted at dinner, barely touching his food. He slanted no teasing glances her way, said nothing more than what was required for polite conversation. It was as if he already wished to put distance between them. Did he fear that after this afternoon she would take advantage of his father's words and insist he marry her?

Another hour passed before the men entered the drawing room. To her dismay, Michael was not among them. She excused herself from the others, and hurried from the room. He was not in the library, nor in the dining room. Finally, she saw a light in Giles's study. She pushed open the door, and stepped inside, blinking as her eyes adjusted to the dim light.

He sat behind Giles's desk, slumped back in the chair, contemplating a glass of brandy in front of him. From the scowl on his face, he seemed to be in no good mood. Rosalyn hesitated.

He looked up, surprise registering on his face. Then he rose to his feet a little awkwardly. 'My dear Rosalyn, I am quite amazed to see you here. I would have thought after my father's surprising announcement you'd wish to avoid me like the plague.'

'I…I had wished to speak with you, but perhaps later.' He was leaning rather heavily against the desk, his dark hair disordered. 'Michael, I think you should return to the drawing room. You do not look at all well.'

He laughed. 'I am quite well. What is it you wish

to talk to me about? Shall I hazard a guess? Our forth-coming nuptials.'

'I assure you, my lord, I have no intention of mar-rying you. There is no need to drink yourself into oblivion over it.'

His eyes glinted. 'Is that what you think? The pos-sibility of marriage to you is pushing me to the bottle?'

'What else am I to think? I have never seen you in this mood before.'

He laughed again, but there was little amusement. 'The notion of marrying me brings you little pleasure, I take it.'

'I do not want a loveless marriage. No more than you do.'

'How do you know what I want?' He stepped closer to her. She could smell the brandy on his breath.

'I suppose I don't really know. I…I think you've had more than enough to drink.'

He advanced a step closer. 'Do you? Since you are not my wife, I cannot imagine why you would care.'

Her hand crept to her locket. She had no idea how to reason with him in such a strange, wild mood. She moistened her dry lips and tried to speak in a rational tone. 'I should not like you to wake up with a head-ache, particularly since we are to leave tomorrow.'

'Always so practical.' He seemed to swoop down upon her. He crushed her against him, his arms bands of iron around her. 'So you don't wish to marry me?'

'No!' She struggled, truly frightened of him for the first time.

'No?' His face hovered before hers, dark and angry and passionate, and then his lips crashed down on hers, demanding her surrender. She tried to break away, then sank against him as his kiss ravished her senses, sending her into a void where there was nothing but him.

He lifted his head, his triumphant eyes glinted down at her. 'What do you say now?'

'I think you are quite drunk! Let go of me!' She struggled against his iron grip.

He abruptly released her. 'Go, Rosalyn.'

She looked at him for an instant, hurt and anger warring in her breast, and then she left him, quietly closing the door behind her.

'Very well, I will be blunt: she doesn't want to marry me,' Michael said. He slumped back in his chair and observed his father grimly. His head felt like hell after last night's drinking, he'd had little sleep, and several cups of strong coffee had done little to abate the dryness in his mouth. The morning sun streaming through the windows of the study made a mockery of his black mood.

'Indeed. Then how did she come to be betrothed to you?' The Duke's voice held little surprise.

'I forced her.'

His father raised a brow. 'How?'

'Her brother lost his estate to me at Fallingham's. She came to me to ask me to return the estate to him— she offered to pay his debts. I refused, of course, and then, based on a passing comment of Charles's decided to return her brother's estate in exchange for a temporary betrothal. I wanted to avoid marriage with Miss Randall. I was in no danger from Rosalyn expecting the engagement to end in marriage; she had made it clear she held me in dislike.'

'I see.'

'You do not seem surprised.'

'Not at all. Margaret had already suspected as much, particularly when she met Lady Jeffreys. Your fian-cée's rather peculiar lack of enthusiasm over your charms, and reluctance to accompany you to the altar, aroused her suspicions. My only question had been what you held over her head.'

Michael laughed shortly. 'Now you know. I plan to release her from the damned betrothal as soon as pos-sible.'

The Duke gave him a considering look. 'I suggest you marry her instead.'

'I have told you, she wishes me to the devil.' Particularly after last night.

'I rather doubt that. How long was this betrothal to go on?'

'Until September. Then she was to have the pleasure of jilting me.'

The Duke smiled dryly. 'You assumed Miss Randall would be safely married by then. However, what was to prevent me from attempting to arrange another match for you?'

'Nothing.' He scowled. 'I suppose you have some-one else in mind.'

'Not at all. I think you and Lady Jeffreys are ad-mirably suited. I see no reason why you cannot use your reputed charm to convince her to marry you. I will give you until the end of this month. After that I will take matters into my own hands.'

Michael gaped at him. Less than three weeks? He shot to his feet. 'I won't have her coerced into mar-riage with me.'

'I have no intention of coercing her.' The Duke also rose, signalling the interview was at an end. 'I will leave you to plot your strategy.' He strode to the door and then turned, his hand on the knob. 'By the way, there was no need for this elaborate scheme to avoid marriage with Miss Randall. If you had indicated you had such a strong aversion to the idea in the first place, I would not have forced you.' He left, gently closing the door behind him.

Michael sunk back down in the chair with a groan. His father had the most interesting ways of accomplishing his goals. If he'd decided Rosalyn was to be the next Marchioness, she would be. Unless she managed to disappear from England. Even then his father would undoubtedly find her. The thought of her joining him at the altar with that white, stricken look on her face made his throat tighten.

But if his father did have his way…afterwards Michael would take her in his arms and assure her marriage to him wouldn't be a living death, that he would protect her and care for her. Then he'd gently kiss her, and she would respond… The hardness in his loins recalled him to his senses.

What the devil was he thinking of? He rubbed his aching head and stood, then paced to the window. He had to come up with something. Only the hell of it was, he had no idea whether he wanted to persuade Rosalyn she must marry him or to spirit her away, safe from his father's reaches.

Chapter Sixteen

'I don't care if she is still abed! I will see her now!'

Rosalyn stiffened. Oh, no! What was her grandmother doing here so early? She turned over and sat up just as the door burst opened.

Lady Carlyn looked livid. In her hand was a newspaper which she brandished about. 'How could you hide this from me? Your own grandmother! Tell me it is nothing but a pack of wicked lies!'

'What is?'

'This!' With a furious finger she jabbed at a point on the paper. 'It says that your brother lost Meryton to Stamford, who is forcing you to marry him as payment! Tell me this is not true!'

'I…I haven't married Stamford yet,' Rosalyn said in a faint voice.

'So it is true! And you never told me! How could you deceive me so!'

'I did not wish to worry you. At any rate, James has Meryton back so there is no need to overset yourself.'

'But to sell yourself into a loveless marriage! And

to a rake who would take such advantage! My dear child, there was no need for such a sacrifice! You should have come to me!'

'Lord Stamford has never taken advantage of me,' Rosalyn said stiffly, offended by hearing Michael spoken of in such terms, although a mere month ago she would have said the same thing herself. 'Besides, I…I am not going to marry him.'

'Not marry him?' Lady Carlyn asked incredulously. 'You have no choice now. If you jilt him, it will only prove the story is true. I won't have it bandied about that my granddaughter had to marry as…as payment for a debt. No, you must marry as soon as possible. I will see Lady Spence about it the first thing.'

A dull throb was beginning in Rosalyn's right temple. 'I would think a marriage would only confirm the story.'

'Nonsense. It will show you don't care a fig for such gossip.' Lady Carlyn eyed Rosalyn sternly. 'I hope you do not plan to stay in bed the entire day with a fit of the vapours. We have several calls to make and a wedding to plan. St James's, I think. You cannot wear white since you are a widow, but perhaps a grey would look becoming.'

'Grandmama! No! I am not going to marry Mi— Lord Stamford. I…I don't want to marry him, and he does not want to marry me. The whole betrothal was a…a farce! He only needed a temporary fiancée and said he would give the estate back if I would agree.' There! She had finally admitted it, but somehow the words gave her little comfort.

Lady Carlyn's mouth fell open, then she snapped it shut. 'Ridiculous!'

'But it is true. So you see, we cannot marry.' Oh, no! Surely she wasn't about cry in front of her grandmother.

Lady Carlyn sighed loudly. 'It is quite obvious that he is in love with you and I dare say, if you weren't so stubborn, you would admit you are in love with him.'

Rosalyn stared at her. 'But, did you not say you thought I was being forced into a…a loveless marriage?'

Lady Carlyn smiled blandly. 'I was merely overset by the shock of reading such a thing in the paper. But, of course, I have known for an age he is in love with you, as does the whole of London. I haven't been quite so certain about you, but now I see how it is.' She patted Rosalyn's hand. 'So there is no need to worry, I shall handle all the arrangements. Perhaps it would be best for you to stay in bed. You shall need all your strength for your wedding, and,' she added with a coy smile, 'your wedding trip.'

'Grandmama, no!' But Lady Carlyn had already risen from the bed and, with a bright smile, bustled out of the room, undoubtedly to arrange the rest of Rosalyn's life.

Rosalyn slumped back on her pillows. Could this whole situation get much worse? They had returned from Longbourne yesterday. She'd had no opportunity to speak to Michael since two nights ago, when he'd kissed her so ruthlessly in Giles's study.

She felt cold every time she thought of that night. His behaviour had been unfathomable to her; she could only think he feared he would somehow be trapped into marriage with her. Yet, he'd seemed so angry when she said she wouldn't marry him.

But her grandmother's supposition that he was in love with her was ridiculous! He could not be! Lady Carlyn always saw what she wanted.

And now the article in the paper! Who would do such a thing? A trap seemed to be closing around her, and around Michael. She must do something.

She had to break off their betrothal.

Watkins showed her into the drawing room, the same one where she'd been shown the very first time she'd ever met him. Butterflies fluttered in her stomach.

Sitting proved impossible. She rose and went to stare at the portrait above the mantelpiece. Now that she knew Michael so well, she could see the resemblance in the same dark, intelligent eyes, the arrogant tilt to the head, the shape of the sensuous mouth.

Then her stomach churned in a sickening manner as she heard his familiar, firm tread. She turned as he came into the room.

He observed her with an unsmiling countenance before coming forward. 'Rosalyn, I had planned to call on you.'

'Did you?' He looked tired, almost as tired as she felt. 'I didn't know, otherwise I…I would not have called on you in such a manner.'

'Since you had no idea of my intentions, I can hardly fault you for that.' His mouth lifted slightly and then he sobered as he observed her face. 'I suppose you saw the piece in the *Morning Post*.'

She nodded and tried to keep her voice from shaking. 'My grandmother called before I had even risen. She was not very pleased.'

'I imagine not. Nor was my father.' He looked at her more closely. 'What is it, Rosalyn?'

She took a deep breath, clutching her reticule in white fingers. 'I want to break off our...our betrothal.'

'Why?'

She stared at him, taken aback by the coldness in his voice. 'Why?'

'Yes, why?' His eyes were cool and wary and he'd folded his arms across his chest in a stance she knew only too well. 'You gave your word until September.'

'I know, but everything has changed. Your father seems to think we...we should marry as soon as possible, and my grandmother...'

'Yes?'

Rosalyn took a deep breath. 'Thinks the same thing after she saw the *Morning Post*. I am afraid that if we do not stop this we...we will find ourselves married.' She twisted her hands in her locket and looked away. 'So I am releasing you from our betrothal. I plan to leave London as soon as possible.'

'If you do that I will bring you back.' There was no denying the threat in his voice. 'Make no mistake, I have no intention of releasing you from our agreement.'

'But...'

'And furthermore, you *are* going to marry me.'

She gaped at him, feeling as if she'd been struck. Was he drunk again? No, he looked perfectly sober and deadly determined, his eyes cool and impassioned. 'I...I beg your pardon?'

'You are going to marry me.'

Marry him? Bewilderment, outrage and hurt flooded through her. And then pure fury. How dare he dictate to her as if she had no say in the matter! 'Marry you? I think not, my lord. I have told you I have no intention of ever marrying again, and certainly not you.'

He stepped towards her. It took every ounce of courage she possessed not to quail at the look on his face. 'Oh, yes, you are,' he said softly. 'Even if I have to force you to the altar.'

'But why? You can't possibly want to marry me!' she blurted out.

'Because after this damned article we have no choice, unless you want a scandal attached to our association. Because my father insists I do so, and moreover—' his eyes ran over her face and deliberately down her body in a way that made her go hot all over as if he had stripped her naked '—because I want you.'

She stepped back, coming up against a side table. The colour drained from her face, leaving her dizzy. 'No.'

'I promise you marriage to me won't be the hell you seem to think,' he went on ruthlessly. 'You will have my title, and you will have my fortune at your disposal. You may come and go as you please.'

'Those things mean nothing to me,' she whispered.

'There will be money to do as you wish with Meryton, then.'

'No, it…it is not worth this.'

'Isn't it?' He came to stand in front of her, almost touching her. She stared at him, helplessly trapped by the table boring into her back. Then he bent his head towards her.

'Michael, please! Don't!' she whispered. He wasn't

going to kiss her again. Not in that angry, ruthless way he had last time as if he meant to force her to his will. She had no idea what was wrong with him. She could only think he was angry that he was somehow trapped. And that he felt a physical desire for her.

He jerked back at her whispered words and stared at her face. Then stepped back, his own face pale. 'Rosalyn, damn it! Don't look at me like that. I won't ravish you.' He moved away from her, running a hand through his hair, then looked back at her. 'I promise I won't touch you after we're married. Except for what is necessary to satisfy society, we need not see each other.'

'No! It...it is impossible.' A cold pit settled in her stomach. Not another marriage of disappointment and waiting, of loneliness. With a strangled sob, she pushed past him and dashed from the room.

Elinor caught her cousin's arm as he headed towards the card room. 'Edmund! I must speak with you! Now!'

Fairchilde looked down at her and gently removed her hand. 'There is no need to clutch me like that. I fear you are wrinkling my coat. Now, what has you in high dudgeon, dear cousin?'

'He is here with her! They are dancing!'

Fairchilde looked at the dancers performing the intricate steps of a quadrille in Lady Carruthers's ball room. His gaze fell on Rosalyn and Stamford, who were circling each other, their faces stiff and unsmiling. 'Yes?'

'They should not be! I thought by now they would not be speaking to each other!'

Fairchilde raised a brow. 'They don't seem to be now.'

'That is not what I meant! They should not even be looking at each other.'

'My dear, did you really think sending that little piece to the *Morning Post* would put an end to their connection?'

'What I meant is I thought you would have done something! She certainly has not fallen into your arms!' Elinor said.

'No.' His lips curled momentarily in a harsh smile, causing Elinor to fall back a pace. Then his usual bland expression returned. 'No, not yet. However, tonight our delightful hostess and one of our most malicious gossips will catch the proper Lady Jeffreys in a flagrant act of impropriety. With myself, of course.'

'Delightful!' Elinor exclaimed, her eyes sparkling with anticipation.

'I thought you would think so.' He gave her a mocking smile. 'So go enjoy yourself with the dull Lord Melton and leave Lady Jeffreys to me.'

Elinor bestowed an excited smile on him and hastened away. Fairchilde watched her for a moment, then turned his attention back to the dancers.

The dance had ended and Stamford was leading Rosalyn from the floor. He watched as Stamford bowed over her hand, then stalked off. Head held high, Rosalyn moved in the opposite direction. Fairchilde smiled. It was high time to make his move.

Rosalyn touched her grandmother's arm. 'I think I will go and sit somewhere. I am rather tired.'

Lady Carlyn turned from her conversation—or,

rather, her monologue—with Miss Waverly, an elderly lady who was hard of hearing and whose conversations mostly consisted of nods and smiles.

'I must admit you do look rather out of curl,' Lady Carlyn said after glancing at Rosalyn's face. 'Well, go and sit, but do not disappear for too long. I don't want everyone to think you are going into a decline after that nasty bit of gossip.'

Rosalyn gave her a wan smile and, after pressing Miss Waverly's frail hand, made her way towards the door leading from the ball room. She was not really ill—so much as she wanted to be alone.

Lady Carruthers's ball room was small and extremely crowded. Rosalyn waited for a pair of giggling debutantes in white muslin gowns to move before she was able to reach the doors. Then she was forced to plaster herself against one of the doors to avoid being slammed into by a stout elderly man in an old-fashioned bagwig. As she stepped away, she felt a tug on the hem of her skirt and then heard an ominous rip. Looking down, she saw the lace on her skirt had caught and torn away.

Could anything else go wrong today? She made her way to the circular hall. She was thankful to see an empty gilt chair. She sank down on it and then bent down to inspect the damage to her hem.

A large strip of lace and ribbons had torn away from the satin material. She would need to call for a maid and obtain some pins to secure the lace. She straightened back up and leaned against the chair with a heavy sigh.

She would rather call the carriage and go home. The only reason she had agreed to attend this ball was that

her grandmother had insisted. 'It will be most noticeable if you do not put in an appearance. Not just for
your sake and, of course, mine, but Stamford's family.
And, my dear, Eversleigh is in town! Why did you not
mention that! He would be most displeased if you are
not there!'

In the end, it was the mention of the formidable
Duke that decided Rosalyn. She had no desire to have
him censure her. Perhaps she could escape this nightmare by fleeing to some remote village in
Northumberland. She closed her eyes. They flew open
as soon as she heard her name.

She looked up to see a bewigged footman standing
in front of her. 'My lady, your grandmother desires
your assistance. If you will follow me.'

She shot up from the chair. 'Oh, no! Is she not
well?'

'I do not know, my lady.'

Worried, she trailed him down the staircase, holding
her skirt so she would not trip on the lace. She barely
acknowledged Miss Markham's greeting as she passed
her and another lady on the stairs. The footman
showed her to a door on the first floor. She thanked
him and pushed open the door.

She saw no one at first glance in the dimly lit room.
It appeared to be some sort of private study. She
moved further in the room and saw the sofa in one
corner was empty. 'Grandmama?'

'I have been waiting for you.'

She jumped as Edmund Fairchilde rose from a chair
at one side of the doorway. He stepped behind her and
shut the door.

She turned, her hand going to her throat in fright and confusion. 'Where is my grandmother?'

He shrugged. 'I have no idea. In the card room, I would imagine.'

'But the footman said she was ill.' He merely looked at her and suddenly she understood. 'You sent that message?'

'Of course. I am certain you are about to ask why. So I will tell you. I have wanted to speak to you alone and this was the only way I could think of to do so.'

'I have no idea what you want to say to me. My brother's debt has been paid.'

His smile caused her to shiver. 'In a manner of speaking, yes. But I still did not get interest. That is what I want to collect tonight.'

'I have no money on me.'

'I said nothing about money. I want something else entirely. Come here, Rosalyn.'

'Let me go. I…I will scream.'

'And I will stop you before you make more than a peep.'

'What do you want?' She had no idea what to do. He was standing in front of the door, blocking her escape.

'A kiss. Nothing more.'

She could scarcely stand to look at him. The thought of his thick lips on hers made her shudder. 'No.'

'Come here now.'

She darted a glance around the room, searching for anything she could use as a weapon. The only item remotely useful was an inkwell sitting on the desk. She backed towards the desk, keeping a wary eye on him. He moved quickly towards her. She snatched up the inkwell just as he reached for her. She darted around the side of the desk as his hand closed around her wrist.

Her foot caught in the torn lace. She tripped backwards, his hand losing its grip on her wrist. He attempted to grab her bodice but she jerked away as his hand closed over the silk rose at her bodice. It tore off in his hand, ripping the silk of her bodice. She darted around the side of the desk, her breathing come in gasps, and held up the inkwell.

Fairchilde laughed, his eyes glittering with a peculiar excitement as if stimulated by the chase. 'That will hardly stop me, my dear.'

'But I will.'

Michael's voice came from the doorway, soft and deadly. Fairchilde turned towards him; for an instant his face registered a deadly hatred. Then his expression became hooded.

'Lady Jeffreys is hardly in need of your assistance,' Fairchilde said in a bored voice. He moved leisurely towards Michael. 'However, I suggest you keep a tighter rein on your fiancée. She is perhaps a bit too free with her favours.'

Michael glanced in her direction, his face filled with a cold, hard fury she'd never seen before. His glance rested on her bodice. With a sickening realisation she saw that the material had torn, revealing her shift beneath. She tried to pull the edges together, feeling as if she were in a horrible nightmare. And her hair had tumbled from its pins.

Michael turned back to Fairchilde. 'I warned you to stay away from her. I protect what is mine. I will have no regrets about putting a bullet through you.'

'You've only to name the place, my lord.'

Rosalyn found her voice. 'No, Michael. Please say no more. This is a misunderstanding. Nothing happened. I cannot bear another scandal.'

His mouth in a tight line, Michael looked over at her. She moved swiftly to his side and touched his arm. 'Please. He…he is not worth it!'

His own features softened slightly as he looked into her pleading face. 'Very well, my dear.' He lifted his head and stared at Fairchilde.

'I'm warning you, Fairchilde. If you come near her again, I will kill you without regret.'

'Is that a challenge?'

'It's a warning. If you value your life at all, you will heed it. I suggest you now remove yourself from the premises or I will throw you out.'

'Not very hospitable, are you? However, I can see I've overstayed my welcome.' Fairchilde moved lazily towards the door, but with a wary look in his eye. He stopped and glanced at Rosalyn.

'I hope you know what you are doing in marrying such a madman.'

Rosalyn closed her eyes, thankful there wasn't to be a duel but afraid Michael's temper would now descend upon herself. If she could have magically transported herself to another country at that moment, she would have done so.

Her legs trembled so hard she feared they would not support her. She swayed and the next thing she knew she was in Michael's arms. He held her for a moment and then asked, 'Did he hurt you?'

'No,' she replied, not looking at him.

'What did he do to you? Did he do this?' He

touched her torn bodice and his gaze hardened as he saw the rent in the skirt of her gown, which by now was beyond simple repair.

'I tore my skirt in the ball room. I…I am fine, really.'

'And your bodice?'

She closed her eyes, ashamed. 'He…he tried to reach for me and…and when I tripped he…he tore the lace.'

She heard his sharp intake of breath. Opening her eyes, she saw he looked furious. 'Damn it, Rosalyn, what were you doing alone in here?'

'A footman said Grandmama was ill. Otherwise, I…I never would have come. Please believe me. I would never have…have willingly gone with him.'

'I know that.' His voice gentled. He stroked her cheek. 'But I fully intend to see he never so much as looks at you again. He will not dare insult my wife.'

'I…I am not going to be your wife.'

'Oh, yes, you are.' He pulled her close and then his mouth descended on hers, his hands tangling in her hair. She made a feeble attempt to shove him away, but his arms only tightened. And his lips, moving gently over hers, were warm and familiar and comforting.

'My dear Lydia! I am certain he said we should find it here. Let me…'

The small shriek caused Rosalyn and Michael to spring apart. Their startled eyes met those of Lady Carruthers and Mrs Bellwood-Smythe, one of London's most notorious gossips.

'I do beg your pardon,' Lady Carruthers gasped, her eyes wide. She backed towards the open door, but Mrs

Bellwood-Smythe's fascinated gaze ran over Rosalyn's dress.

'Oh, my! Are you all right, my dear?'

Rosalyn flushed. 'Oh, yes. I…I merely tore my dress in the ball room.'

'Of course.' Mrs Bellwood-Smythe's expression was one of complete disbelief.

'Lydia!' Lady Carruthers grabbed her arm and pulled her from the room.

Michael stared after their retreating backs, his face stunned, then seemed to come to his senses. He strode to the door, closing it firmly behind them.

His gaze was impassive as he turned towards Rosalyn. 'That settles it. By tomorrow the entire *ton* will most likely think I was attempting to rip your clothes from your body and ravish you in Lord Carruthers's study. I'll be damned before I let you leave me with that hanging over my head.' A peculiar smile twisted his lips. 'You have no choice but to wed me after tonight, my dear.'

Chapter Seventeen

Rosalyn sat on the edge of her bed, dressed only in her shift and petticoat. She supposed she should ring for Annie to help her to dress for the dinner party she was to attend. She had only meant to lie down and close her eyes for a few minutes; instead, she'd slept for nearly two hours.

She heaved herself off the bed and rang the bell. Caroline was holding a small dinner party for family. Nothing very formal, she had reassured Rosalyn.

Ever since the Carruthers's ball five days ago, his family had gone out of their way to protect her from the gossip surrounding the whole disaster. Despite the efforts of Lady Spence and the Duke of Eversleigh, the rumours had run wild all over London. As Michael had predicted, Mrs Bellwood-Smythe had spread it about that Rosalyn had been locked in a passionate embrace with him, her gown ripped from her bodice, the rest left to everyone's sordid imagination. The more nasty-minded believed he had tried to ravish her.

Which was why she could not bring herself to run away from London. Such action would only serve to confirm the rumours. And she could not do that to Michael.

She'd refused, however, to discuss the wedding. Lady Spence had unexpectedly come to her rescue, saying Rosalyn needed a few days to herself. She had been seen in public only once with Michael. Rosalyn had forced herself to smile and nod and take his arm as if nothing had happened.

'My lady, what will you wear? The cream gown or perhaps the one of sea-green?' Annie's voice interrupted her reverie.

'Oh, the green, I think.' She watched Annie bustle around. At least the Season had proved beneficial for one person—Annie had quite turned from a shy country miss to a very competent lady's maid. Rosalyn hadn't the heart to tell her yet that she would most likely never be the lady's maid to a Marchioness.

Annie helped her into the gown, then dressed her hair in an elaborate knot on top of her head. After that, she retrieved Rosalyn's jewel box and brought it to her. Rosalyn's eye fell on the rose brooch Michael had given her. She touched it, feeling unexpectedly sad.

Annie peered over her shoulder. 'It is so pretty, my lady. Do you wish to wear it?'

'I don't know. Yes, I think I will.' She pinned it to her bodice, her thoughts straying to Michael. She had spent no time alone with him, almost as if there was some sort of conspiracy to keep them apart. Either her grandmother was with her, or one of his relations. He had not once called on her. His manner was polite, almost too polite. He seemed a stranger.

After Annie finished with her toilette, Rosalyn picked up her gloves, fan, and shawl and went down to her drawing room. Her grandmother should be arriving soon and Rosalyn would share her carriage.

Lost in thought, she jumped at the sound of a rap on the door. She gathered her things and went to the hallway where Mrs Harrod had opened the door. 'And where is Frederick?' she was asking.

''E's been taken ill. I've come for her ladyship.'

Rosalyn gave Mrs Harrod a distracted smile as she stepped past her into the night air. A light misty rain was falling as she reached the carriage. She stopped, puzzled, for the carriage was completely unfamiliar. Her grandmother did not seem to be inside. She turned as a terrible uneasiness assailed her.

Then she screamed as a hand clamped over her mouth. She was pulled up against a hard chest, then shoved into the coach. The door slammed shut, and she fell against the cushions as the horses sprang away.

Michael stood next to the mantelpiece in Caroline's drawing room, every nerve in his body on edge, as Lady Carlyn was announced. He'd been waiting for Rosalyn, worrying about her. Always quiet, she had seemed to be in some sort of daze ever since that damnable night at the Carruthers's ball. He had no idea how to reach her, afraid if he touched her he wouldn't be able to stop. And like a coward, he'd avoided spending time alone with her. He had no intention of giving her the chance to tell him she would not marry him.

He frowned. Lady Carlyn had come alone. There was no Rosalyn. Was she unwell? Or couldn't she bear the thought of facing his family one more time? Facing him? He'd hoped she would come so he could tell her he'd finally tracked down James. He hoped the news James had been at Meryton since he had left Newmarket would jolt her out of her trance.

He moved across the drawing room to Lady Carlyn's side. She was smiling and talking to his aunt, apparently unperturbed by Rosalyn's absence. 'I had the most dreadful time persuading her to accompany me to the dressmaker's! And then she would not look at anything! Sometimes I vow she is—' She broke off to address Michael. 'I really should not say such things about your bride-to-be! But really, she can be most difficult, I should warn you.'

'Where is she?' Michael asked.

Lady Carlyn looked puzzled. 'Who?'

'Rosalyn. I thought she was to come with you.'

Lady Carlyn looked surprised. 'Really? But you had sent a note around saying that you would send a carriage for her. I must admit I was rather relieved as it meant I needn't rush around so much.' She peered around him as if expecting to see Rosalyn behind him. 'But she is not here?'

'I sent no note.'

'Of course you did. It arrived—why yes, it arrived just as I returned from shopping. I remember because the footman gave it to me just as I stepped into the drawing room. I was quite surprised.'

'Where is the note?'

'I have no idea. I suppose I tossed it away.' His meaning finally seemed to penetrate her mind. 'You did not send a note? But who would?'

'Michael?' Lady Spence looked worried.

'I have no idea,' he said shortly.

Then his blood ran cold. Fairchilde? But would he stoop to such a thing? The man's cold determination, the vision of him reaching for Rosalyn, flashed sickeningly though his mind. And Fairchilde hated him.

'Michael? What is wrong?' Lady Spence touched his arm, her face full of worry.

'I must go.' He shook off her arm and started towards the door. 'I have to find her.'

He dashed down the winding staircase to the hallway, only pausing to call for his overcoat. He carried a pistol in its pocket. Outside he nearly collided with James Whitcomb, who was running up the steps. James's face was white, his cravat in complete disarray.

'Thank God you're here. He has Rosalyn!' James sounded sick with fear.

'Fairchilde?' At James's nod, Michael said, 'How can you be certain?'

'I just arrived in London. I wanted to call on her, apologise to her, but when I got there…the housekeeper said she saw him seize her. Or at least she thought it was him. But who else would do such a thing?' All trace of the cynical, wild young man had vanished. He looked more like a frightened school boy. 'It is all my fault! God! If I hadn't invited him to Meryton, hadn't lost the money—'

'Never mind that now! I will find her.'

'I'm coming with you!'

Michael looked at him. 'Very well. Then…' He spun around and saw Charles, Philip, and Giles behind him, their faces grim.

'Thought we might be of assistance,' Charles said. 'Where to?'

'Ask Rosalyn's housekeeper if she has any information. I'm going to Fairchilde's. Meet me there.'

And he was going to kill Fairchilde.

But Fairchilde was not there. His manservant, a beefy man with a surly expression, was disinclined to talk until Charles shoved him up against the hallway wall. Michael levelled a pistol at his heart.

'Won't do you much good if I'm dead, will it?' the man said with a smirk.

Michael cocked the pistol. 'It matters little to me whether you are or not. I'm certain there are others who'll be willing to tell me what I want to know.'

The bravado left the man's face as he looked at Michael's cold, unwavering gaze. 'Darley Hall,' he finally spat out.

Charles met Michael's eyes. 'Does that sound right?'

'Yes.'

Charles released the man, and they dashed from the house.

Darley Hall. Of course. It was Fairchilde's estate, a little more than two hours north of London. He prayed they'd reach her in time. For he dreaded to think what Fairchilde intended to do to her.

Rosalyn was jolted as the carriage hit a rut. Fear kept her immobilised in a corner as she tried to stay as far away as possible from Edmund Fairchilde. He had not tried to touch her, only watched her with his cold, hooded eyes.

They had left London. She could scarcely see where they were; the night was dark, the passing scenery only an occasional shadow. Fear combined with the lack of food and the motion of the carriage made her feel slightly nauseous.

She shivered, forcing herself to speak. 'Wh...where are you taking me?'

'You shall see when we get there,' he said.

'Why? Why are you doing this to me?'

She could barely see his mouth curve in an unpleasant smile. 'Revenge.'

'Revenge? I...I have done nothing to you.'

'Oh, you have, my dear. It would have been better for you if you had accepted my first offer. I do not like to be thwarted. And in this case, revenge shall be particularly sweet as I shall enjoy snatching you from Stamford. He has long been a thorn in my side, and his latest attempts to ruin me have most seriously displeased me. Instead, he is the one that will be ruined.'

Rosalyn wrapped her cloak more tightly about herself. 'I...I have no idea why abducting me would ruin him.' Perhaps if she kept him talking, she could discover some clue, some idea that would enable her to escape him.

'He is in love with you, my dear. Knowing that you are in my hands, at my mercy, knowing I am enjoying your delights, will cause him to suffer exceedingly. Particularly when he realises there is nothing he can do about it.'

'You are wrong. He does not love me. We are not going to be married.'

'You are correct in that regard. You will not marry Stamford.'

She moistened her dry lips. She had to ask. 'Wh...what are you planning to do with me?'

His eyes roved over her in a way that made her skin crawl. 'Bed you, of course. Perhaps I will marry you myself.'

Sick revulsion flooded her being. 'You cannot force me to do that.'

He laughed unpleasantly. 'Oh, I can. There are many ways. A dose of laudanum, perhaps. Whisky. None of it may be necessary. You may decide after a few nights in my bed you will be most willing to marry me.'

She lifted her chin. 'I doubt that.'

He laughed again. 'Shall we see? Come here, Rosalyn.'

'No!' Her stomach lurched along with the carriage. She tried to fold herself into the corner as far as she could.

'Come, or I will make you sorry you didn't obey me.' He made a move toward her.

'I...I feel quite ill,' she said faintly. Indeed, she did. She feared if he touched her, she would be sick all over him.

He stared at her, then settled back in his corner, apparently deciding she was serious. A moment later, he shot up as the coach lumbered to a halt.

'What the devil!' He grabbed a pistol hanging from its leather near his seat.

'Stand and deliver!'

'Blast it!' He turned and flashed a hard glance at Rosalyn. 'Stay there!' He pushed his pistol through the window and fired.

The coach door on the opposite side was yanked opened. Rough hands pulled Rosalyn from her seat at the same time she heard more shots. She was vaguely aware of Fairchilde tumbling back. Frantic, she tried to aim a kick at her attacker.

'Rosalyn! Damn it! It's me!'

'James?' She collapsed into his arms, shaking. He hugged her close.

'My God! Are you all right? He didn't harm you?'

'No. Oh, James, what are you doing here?'

'I came with Stamford.'

'Michael?'

'Yes. I'm sorry, Rosalyn.' He pulled away from her, his face haggard with shock and worry. 'This is all my doing.'

'Oh, no! You…you don't know how I…I worried about you!' She clutched at him.

'Whitcomb? Do you have her?' She recognised Philip's voice.

'Yes. She's safe.'

'Bring her here. We need you to cover the coach. Michael's been shot!'

'No!' The sound was torn from her. She jerked out of her brother's arms, and stumbled around the back of the coach.

She saw his figure on the ground, heard a low moan. Philip, kneeling beside him, looked up as she ran to his side. She dropped to her knees, heedless of the muddy road. Fear clutched her when she saw the dark stain spreading down the left arm of his evening coat. 'Michael!'

He was sitting up, half-supported by Philip. He looked at her, his eyes glazed with pain. 'You're safe?'

'Oh, yes. Michael, please…' she whispered.

'We need to get him out of his coat. Can you help me?' Philip said.

'Yes.'

Michael swore. 'Get away, Rosalyn.'

'Be quiet,' she told him sharply.

She helped Philip ease him out of his coat, her heart in her throat. Philip ripped the sleeve from his shirt exposing his arm. A gasp escaped her at the sight of the raw ragged hole in his arm just below the shoulder.

'We need to stop the bleeding.' Philip was making a pad of his neckcloth. 'Ask the others for cravats, shirts, if we must, anything.'

'Yes.' She rose, almost running into Charles. He heard her request and without a word removed his cravat. She took it, then kneeled.

Caught in a nightmare, she tried to help as Philip attempted to stem the blood seeping from the wound. The voices of the others, the mud of the road, the light misty rain receded from her consciousness as she passed strip after strip of dry cloth to Philip. Michael said nothing, but she could see from the way he gripped her hand and the set look of his mouth it was all he could do to remain silent.

At last, Philip bound the arm with a strip of her shawl. He looked up as Charles approached.

'How is he?' Charles asked.

'It should hold, but we need to get him to a surgeon. The shot is still in his arm. Where's Fairchilde?'

'Bound up near the coach. Giles shot him in the leg after he shot Michael. Only a flesh wound,' Charles said. His easy manner was gone, his eyes were hard. 'What should we do with him?'

Michael struggled to sit up. 'I shall be glad to dispose of him,' he said grimly.

'Although I fully comprehend your sentiments, we

don't need a murder to complicate matters,' Philip said. He stood. 'How far is Darley Hall?'

'Michael?' Charles asked.

'A half-hour's ride,' Michael said. He had slumped back against Rosalyn, his face drained, the spurt of energy he'd shown at Fairchilde's name now spent.

'We'll leave him a horse and take the carriage. He can make his way to Darley Hall,' Philip said. He looked down at Rosalyn. 'Can you manage him for a moment? Don't let him move.'

'No,' she said.

The rest of the trip passed in a haze. Michael could not be laid in the coach, so they made him as comfortable as possible, tucking coats under his head so he could rest his head in one corner. Rosalyn sat at his side, refusing to leave him, trying her best to cushion the jolts. He remained conscious, and then finally collapsed in the corner, eyes closed. Philip sat across from her, James next to him, pale and worried.

Once Philip leaned forward and touched her knee. 'Don't worry, Rosalyn. I've seen worse. He'll pull through.'

She nodded, her heart numb. Because if he didn't, she had no idea how she would survive. For she realised, with utter overwhelming clarity, she loved him.

Chapter Eighteen

His arm ached. He slowly opened his eyes and realised, with some wonder, he was in his own bed. He had no idea what time it was or the day. He vaguely remembered voices coming and going, but time had passed in a hazy, drugged stupor. The last thing he remembered before fainting as the surgeon cut into his arm was Rosalyn's white face hovering over him.

He must have made a sound for he heard the rustle of skirts, and then his eyes focused vaguely on a familiar figure.

'Michael, are you awake? Do you know me?' His aunt Margaret hovered over him, lines of concern on her drawn face.

'Yes,' he managed to whisper.

She passed a gentle hand over his forehead. 'Your fever has finally broken.' She knelt by him. 'We have been so worried. I am so thankful you are awake.'

'How long...?'

'Three days. You developed a fever after the surgeon removed the bullet. You have been very ill,

Michael.' She brought him a glass of water. 'Can you drink?'

She helped him take a few sips, then he fell back on the pillows, willing himself not to drift into another sleep.

He closed his eyes, then they shot open. 'Rosalyn. Where is she?'

'She is here. She has been staying with us since the night you were wounded. Can you take a little more water?'

He pushed her hand away. 'I must see her.'

'Michael! I think it would be best if you waited.' She sighed as he attempted to throw back the covers. 'Very well, don't agitate yourself. I shall fetch her.'

Rosalyn quietly closed the door behind her. Michael lay very still, his eyes closed. He turned his head as she approached the bed and opened his eyes. His usually olive skin was pale and his hair, unruly under the best of circumstances, tumbled over his forehead in complete disorder.

'Rosalyn.' She had to bend to catch his voice. 'Did he hurt you?'

'No, I am quite safe.' His pallor and weakness alarmed her. She fought back tears that were all too close.

'I am glad.' He fumbled for her hand. 'Sit by me. I must talk to you.'

She sunk down in the chair by his bed. 'Not now. You need to rest. You have been very ill.'

He focused on her, his eyes drugged from the laudanum he'd been given to dull his pain. 'Stay with me.'

'I will. Please try to rest, Michael.' She smoothed his hair back from his brow, and he closed his eyes.

Rosalyn sat with him for a long while, as she had for the past few interminable days. The candles slowly burned down, casting a soft glow in the room. His breathing was slow and even, and he no longer tossed and turned in feverish delirium as he had been doing during the past few days.

She stroked his hand, then brought it to her cheek for a moment, tears of thankfulness streaming down her face. For the first time since that terrible night, she had hope that he would live.

After a while, Caroline tiptoed in to relieve her, touching her hand in passing. Unable to sleep, Rosalyn wandered down to the library. She was startled to find the Duke still up, idly browsing through a book. He laid it aside when she entered.

After a few days in his company, Rosalyn could understand why his family found him daunting. Although his dark hair was flecked with silver, he very much resembled his sons, possessing the same handsome, aristocratic features. But it was his inborn air of self-assurance and command, coupled with the penetrating look in his grey eyes, that inspired awe in those around him. At first she had thought him a very hard man, but she had seen the lines of worry in his face for his son and knew he would be devastated if Michael were not to live.

'Lady Jeffreys,' he said politely, as he rose to his feet. 'How do you find my son?'

'He is much better; not so feverish and restless but so very weak. I still worry for him.'

'The surgeon assured us once the fever has broken,

the worst is over. Stamford is a survivor with a will of iron.' He put a hand on her shoulder. 'You should go to bed, my dear. You look peaked.'

She tried to smile. 'I do not think I can sleep.'

'What is troubling you?' he asked quietly.

'I cannot help but feel this whole affair is my fault. If it had not been for me, he would not have nearly been killed.'

'I do not believe you deliberately attracted Fairchilde's attentions, did you?'

'No, never.' She shuddered. 'He was quite the most repugnant man I have ever met.'

'You surely cannot hold yourself responsible for the harm he wished to do you and Michael? That would be most foolish and quite unnecessary. You are only fortunate that Michael and the others found you in time.'

'Yes.' She was silent and looked directly at him. 'It is not that, your Grace. You see, Michael and I, we…we really were never betrothed. It was only a temporary bargain between us. He wished to avoid marriage with Miss Randall, I wanted my brother's estate back…' Her voice trailed away as he held up his hand.

'I know this, my dear. Michael told me before we left Longbourne.'

'Oh, dear.'

'He feared I would coerce you to the altar so he felt he should inform me of the truth.'

'Oh, what must you think of me?' she whispered. Her hands crept to her burning cheeks. 'I am so very sorry for such deceit. And then for Michael to almost lose his life because of it.'

'My dear, this is nonsense. You have nothing to reproach yourself for. If anything, I am grateful he has met you.' He smiled slightly, his eyes kind. 'I suggest you retire now. Wearing yourself out with worry will not help.'

He held the door open for her, and as she passed he said, 'I trust you care for him?'

She looked up at him, a blush heating her cheeks. 'Yes, very much.'

He touched her cheek. 'That is all that matters. Good night.'

Four days later, Rosalyn stood in the doorway of the sitting room off Michael's bedchamber. He sat in a wing-chair, facing the window looking out over the garden behind Eversleigh House. He did not turn until she came into the room.

'Rosalyn.' He made a move to rise.

'Please don't. I know you are still not recovered.' He looked much better, but she could see he was still pale. He wore a dark-green silk dressing gown over his loose white shirt and breeches. His arm was in a sling under the gown. 'I will not stay very long.'

'No. I did not think you would.' He looked at her with that unreadable expression he'd had on his face the last two days, ever since he started to recover from his fever. He was polite, but remote, as if his whispered request for her to stay at his side had never happened.

She swallowed her despair and managed a smile. 'I know James has thanked you, but I also wanted to thank you for what you have done for James.

Particularly after he did lose more money at Newmarket. You did not need to return Meryton.'

'I have no great desire to worry about another property. I thought it fitting punishment he should learn how to manage the place properly.' A cool smile touched his lips. 'We will see how grateful James is after a few months. Rutherford is one of my best stewards, which is why I have sent him to Meryton. He is a good man, but a hard taskmaster. James will find there is little time for gambling. However, he could not have a better tutor for learning how to run an estate.'

'I am certain it will be quite good for him.'

'I hope it keeps him out of trouble.' Michael returned his gaze to the window.

'Yes.' She moved next to his chair. 'He felt responsible for Fairchilde's obsession as he invited him to Meryton. It is nonsense, but it seems to have sobered him considerably.'

Michael glanced up at her. 'If he ever does anything else that puts you in danger like that, I'll have him whipped.'

'I doubt he will.' She took a deep breath, clasping her hands together. 'There is something else I must tell you. I…I think I will go to Meryton for a while.'

'Why?'

'There is no point in continuing here. Your father knows about our agreement, and Miss Randall is to marry Mr Redding. I am so grateful to you…'

'I don't want your gratitude,' he interrupted her. He turned to look at her, a dark look on his face. 'Nor do I care about Miss Randall's nuptials.'

'What do you want?' she whispered.

He rose from the chair, staggering a little. Alarmed for him, she caught his arm. He shook her off and before she could think, caught her to him, his good arm pulling her tight against him. He looked down into her face, his eyes no longer indifferent, but dark with passion. 'This is what I want.'

His lips crushed hers in a fierce kiss, surprisingly masterful for a man who was still convalescing. Not wanting to struggle for fear of doing him further injury, Rosalyn decided she had no choice but to yield to his embrace.

He didn't let her go until a slight sound made them pull apart. He lifted his head, and they both turned towards the door.

Eversleigh stood there, eyeing them with an unreadable expression. 'I would not interrupt you longer than necessary. I take it, however, you have no objections if your wedding takes place tomorrow.'

Rosalyn felt the colour drain from her face. She stole a glance at Michael, who had turned to stone. Then an odd smile touched his mouth. 'But I do, sir. If you will excuse me, Rosalyn, I would like to speak to my father alone.'

'Yes.' In a daze, she left the room.

Michael watched her go, then turned to his father. 'This is impossible.'

The Duke walked over to the chair. 'I suggest you sit down before you faint. Then you may tell me why. After the embrace I just witnessed, I could be forgiven for assuming the matter has been settled.'

Michael flushed, and sat down. 'Hardly. I told her after the damnable ball she must marry me in order to save her reputation and mine. She probably would have looked more delighted if I'd informed her she'd be facing a firing squad.'

'Your usual address seems to have been somewhat lacking,' Eversleigh said. 'However, I trust you will remedy the matter after you are married.'

'We are not going to be married.'

'I am loathe to contradict you, but you will be. You are quite correct in attempting to save your reputation, particularly if you persist in kissing her in your bed-chamber or in private rooms at balls.'

'I promise to stay away from her. She wishes to leave for Meryton at any rate.' He ran an agitated hand through his hair as he saw his father's imperturbable expression. 'It's impossible! I won't have her coerced. I know how persuasive you can be.'

The Duke raised thin brows. 'I have no intention of coercing her. She will not be unwilling, I think. I am correct in assuming you love her?'

'I love her more than anything. Too much to force her into marriage.'

'The wedding will be small. Family and a few friends. I suggest you rest.'

Michael rose, agitated. 'I must talk to Rosalyn. I must make certain this is what she wishes.'

His father moved to the door and paused, his hand resting on the doorknob. 'You may speak with her tomorrow. There will be time enough to settle your concerns after you are wed.' He closed the door firmly behind him.

Michael sank down into his chair and buried his head in his hands. She should have made her escape while he was unconscious. Once his father decided on a course of action there was no thwarting him. Michael only prayed she did not hate him too much.

Tension filled him. Not so much with worry that there would be a wedding tomorrow, but from fear there would not.

Rosalyn sat on a sofa in the library, her gaze fixed on a statue of Shakespeare. She started when she heard soft footsteps, and turned to see Lady Spence enter the room.

Lady Spence smiled down at Rosalyn, then seated herself next to her. Her eyes held sympathy. 'Are you all right, my dear? I fear my brother can be somewhat overwhelming when he has his mind made up.'

'He…he wishes us to be married tomorrow,' Rosalyn whispered.

'I know. I will admit it is rather sudden, but I do think it is for the best.' She touched Rosalyn's hand. 'Michael loves you very much, you know.'

'He…he has never said anything.'

'Perhaps he is not certain of your feelings. He worries about forcing you into a marriage you don't want.' Her gaze was direct. 'If you are certain you don't wish to marry him, if you can say you do not love him, then I will put a halt to the wedding.'

'No, I…I cannot say that,' Rosalyn whispered. 'But surely the Duke told you. We never meant to marry.'

'I had already guessed that, even before Alistair confirmed it. My dear, I know this is not what either of you had planned. But sometimes fate plays us a much different hand than we expect. We cannot control everything, even the events we set in motion ourselves. You and Michael will be married. You are meant for each other. I have thought so from the first. Sometimes it is no use trying to run from our lives; you could go on like this and both of you would be unhappy. It will be best to wed tomorrow and start your lives together.'

Further argument seemed futile. In her own quiet way, Lady Spence was as strong as her brother. No wonder Michael had resorted to a false engagement to avoid an unwanted marriage. And when Watkins announced Lady Carlyn, and Rosalyn saw her grandmother bustle in, a pleased and determined look on her face, Rosalyn knew her fate was sealed. Fighting the three of them would be impossible.

And in her heart, she had no desire to do so.

Chapter Nineteen

Annie fastened the tapes of the dove-grey silk wedding dress Rosalyn wore and then bent to arrange the skirts. Lady Spence and Caroline fluttered around her. Her hair was tied in a knot at the top of her head and fell in dark ringlets to her shoulders. Caroline wove a circlet of fragrant lily-of-the-valley through her hair. Lady Spence fastened a strand of pearls around her neck.

Lady Carlyn entered the bedchamber and bustled forward to catch Rosalyn's hands. 'How lovely you look! So like your mother, I vow I could cry!' She kissed Rosalyn's cheek, her own moist with tears.

She stepped away, pressing a small picture frame into Rosalyn's hand. Rosalyn saw it was a miniature of her mother as a very young woman. She looked up at her grandmother with misty eyes. 'Thank you.'

'I only hope you will be as happy as your mother was in her marriage.'

'Grandmama?'

Lady Carlyn smiled sheepishly through her tears. 'Well, I could see she was. Anyone could.'

Rosalyn hugged her grandmother, tears springing to her eyes.

And then Caroline was kissing her on the cheek and telling her how beautiful she was and how she looked forward to having her for a sister. Lady Julianna, Michael's youngest sister, came in and presented her with a bouquet of fragrant pale pink roses to carry and pressed her hand. Finally, Lady Spence pronounced her ready and took her arm.

Michael stood at the front of the drawing room where the guests were assembled, waiting for his bride. Only vaguely aware of the others, his eyes were fixed on the doors. Time seemed to tick by ruthlessly and still Rosalyn did not come. Perhaps she had managed to escape after all, he thought with sick despair.

Finally the doors were flung open, and his sisters and aunt entered, followed by Lady Carlyn and James, and to his great, overwhelming relief, Rosalyn. She was beautiful; her dark hair tied in a loose knot tumbled to her shoulders, the colour of her dress enhanced the pale perfection of her skin. She drifted towards him like one in a trance, and he briefly wondered if they had drugged her.

He took her hand as she joined him in front of the priest—it was ice cold. Her gaze, as she met his own, was bewildered. He wanted to take her in his arms then and there and comfort her, but it would have to wait until after the ceremony.

For Rosalyn, the wedding passed in a dream. The only solid and real thing was Michael, standing pale and still beside her, his arm in a sling under his morn-

ing coat. His hand was warm and firm around hers as
the priest began to recite the words of the age-old ceremony. She heard Michael repeat the vows, 'I,
Michael Stephen Elliot...' and then the priest turned
to her. She must have hesitated too long for Michael
squeezed her hand. He leaned toward her, 'Rosalyn,
please.' She saw the vulnerability in his face and
snapped out of her inertia to obediently repeat her
vows. He slipped the ring on her finger.

And then they were pronounced man and wife.
Michael bent over her and his lips were on hers, gentle
and comforting.

The guests adjourned to the dining room. On such
short notice, Lady Spence, with help from her nieces
and Lady Carlyn, had organised an elaborate wedding
breakfast. Lady Spence instructed the bridal couple to
sit at the centre of one of the long sides of the heavy
mahogany table.

Glancing at Michael, Rosalyn thought he appeared
unnaturally pale. He had not said much to her, and
appeared as shell-shocked as she felt. Had his father
caught him in a moment of delirium and told him he
was to marry her? The thought was too awful to con-
template.

'You are not eating, Rosalyn,' said Michael.

She glanced at his plate, which was as untouched
as hers. She could not remember how the food came
to be in front of her. 'Neither are you.'

He grimaced. 'I find I have little appetite. It is difficult to eat when one is the centre of so much attention. We should have eloped and avoided the fuss.'

She laughed shakily. 'I don't think your father
would have liked that. Or my grandmother either.'

'You are quite right. And in my condition I don't think I could have managed to escape out of the window, unfortunately. It would not be very romantic to have your bridegroom faint on you.'

'Very unromantic and very inconvenient.'

He leaned towards her. 'Would you have come with me, Rosalyn?' he asked softly.

She caught her breath, sudden shyness overtaking her, and looked down at her hands.

'May I propose a toast to the bride and groom?' Rosalyn started as Charles's voice boomed out over the chattering of the guests. He grinned at them, lifting his champagne glass.

Several more speeches followed, expressing wishes for future happiness and congratulations, and then Caroline and Lady Spence were at Rosalyn's side. Caroline took her hand and whispered they would escort her upstairs. She rose from the table, and Michael stood up.

Lady Spence frowned at him. 'You had best repair to your chamber. You look as if you are about to collapse. That will hardly do.'

'I have no intention of collapsing.' But Rosalyn did not like the white look about his mouth. 'I would like to speak with my wife in private, if you please.'

'You may later. After you rest,' Lady Spence replied firmly.

'Do not worry. We are not about to spirit her away,' Caroline told him patting his arm. 'She also needs to rest.'

'Of course.' He fixed Rosalyn with an anxious gaze—almost, she thought in surprise, as if he thought she would vanish.

She gave him a small, reassuring smile, then turned to go with Caroline.

'Is there anything more you need, my lady? I hope the room is satisfactory' the housekeeper said, giving Rosalyn an anxious glance. Rosalyn started from her daze, realising she had said nothing since entering the bedchamber.

'Thank you, it is lovely.' Some time during the afternoon, her belongings had been moved from the guest chamber she had occupied to the room adjoining the sitting room next to Michael's chamber. It was a beautiful room, decorated in shades of rose, cream and gold. After the housekeeper departed, she sank down on the four-poster bed hung with rose and cream hangings. Strange to think this was now her home, her room.

Lady Spence knocked and entered. She came to sit next to Rosalyn, touching her hand. 'You must be exhausted. I shall send your abigail to draw your bath and help you into your nightclothes.' She smiled gently at Rosalyn. 'We thought it would be best if you and Michael had some time alone without the others. Particularly since Michael will not be able to travel for a few more days. I know everything has been very confusing for both of you and there has been little time to recover yourselves. Eversleigh and Julianna shall stay with me. If you need anything, you have only to send a servant around.'

'But Michael…he is still not very well,' Rosalyn stammered, panicked. How could she stay here with him alone? She had thought at least his family would be here until they could sort through this mess.

'He will be fine. Just make certain he doesn't over-
exert himself and keep him in bed as much as possible.
I am certain you'll have no trouble managing him.'
She arose from the bed and kissed Rosalyn's cheek.
Eversleigh and Julianna entered, and bade her good-
bye, and then she was quite alone.

Annie came in to undress Rosalyn and draw her
bath. After that she helped Rosalyn into an ivory
nightdress and dressing gown.

'How very pretty,' said Annie, touching the fine
lawn material. She noticed her mistress's expression.
'Lady Carlyn gave me the package. She said it was
for you to wear tonight.'

'I see.' Oh, dear. Why had her grandmother given
her such an intimate gift? No, she knew why.

The room felt deserted after Annie left. The ticking
of the clock emphasised the awful quiet. She stared
out the window and wondered what she should do
next. Never had she felt more alone in her life.

She had not seen Michael since the wedding. Did
he not wish to see her? Or perhaps he had fallen ill
again. As much as she wished she could avoid him,
she could not. She must talk to him.

She looked down at the soft folds of her nightclothes and wished she was wearing something more
practical, such as a high-necked cotton dress. If she
went to his bedchamber dressed like this, he might
think she wanted to seduce him. How humiliating! She
had no idea what their relationship was to be.

Rosalyn searched through the wardrobe and finally
found a large paisley shawl and threw it over her
gown. She opened the connecting door and nearly collided with Michael. She gasped.

Michael caught her with his good arm. 'It is only me. My dear girl, whatever is wrong?'

'I am sorry. I did not expect to see you there.' She backed away from him and pulled the shawl more firmly about her shoulders, then folded her arms across her chest. He closed the door behind him and stood with his back to it.

'Were you by any chance coming to see me?' he asked. He wore a dressing gown in a rich shade of burgundy. The light from the candles gleamed off his dark hair. He was partially in the shadows, and she could not see the expression on his face.

She felt her knees tremble but tried to keep her voice calm. 'I must talk to you. It could wait until tomorrow, however. I am certain you must be quite tired. I know I am.'

He advanced towards her, and she backed away. He caught her hand. 'Come and sit down. I think we should talk now and not put this off any longer.' He pulled her down beside him on the side of her bed. She clutched the shawl with nervous fingers.

'There is no need to look so frightened, Rosalyn,' he said with gentle amusement in his voice. 'Tell me what's troubling you.'

'Michael, I am not certain how this happened. We were not supposed to be married,' she said faintly.

'Isn't it obvious? My father decided we were to be married and we were. I only hope he did not cow you into this.'

'Oh, no,' she replied on a slight laugh. 'Not your father, your aunt. She seemed to consider the matter settled, and I could see no way of arguing with her.'

He brushed the hair back from her face with gentle

fingers. 'We hadn't a chance between the two of them. They can be thwarted, but one usually needs a little time to plan a strategy. In this case, time was short— and I did not wish to thwart them.'

He caressed her hand, making slow circles around her thumb with a finger. It was very distracting. She pulled her mind back to the subject at hand. 'But you didn't wish to be married. You wanted this bargain so you could avoid it.'

'Yes, caught in my own trap.' He moved closer to her. 'But I think I shall like my trap very much as long as I am trapped with you.' He reached up and slowly slipped the shawl off her shoulders. 'Must you wear this? If you are cold there are other ways to keep you warm.'

Actually, she was not cold at all—she felt hot and vulnerable. He slowly caressed her cheek, sending little sparks of fire down her spine. 'Will it really be such a terrible fate to have me for a husband, Rosalyn? I take my vows very seriously. I fully intend to love, honour, and cherish you, to remain faithful to you for the rest of my life.'

'You wished to marry me?' she whispered.

'Yes, more than anything, for a very long time. Perhaps even from the first.'

'Michael, I…'

He bent and gently kissed her lips. 'I know you have doubts about marriage. I vow I will not leave you if that is what you fear. I plan to live a long, long time. And I will not desert you in any other way. You will not be alone and left to your own devices. You are my wife and a part of me, as I wish to be a part of you.'

Tears sprang to her eyes. 'Oh, Michael,' she whispered.

His hand slid the robe off her shoulders. 'I love you. Do you suppose you could learn to love me more than a little, Rosalyn?'

'Yes, I think so.' Somehow, she found herself eased against the pillows and Michael stretched out fully beside her. His dressing gown had fallen from his shoulders revealing a dark mat of hair curling on his bare chest. She glanced down and blushed to see he was wearing nothing at all under his robe. Her stomach tightened as he pulled her to him and kissed her with fierce, hungry passion.

Her eyes closed and she moved her hands shyly down his chest, then over his arm. Her lids snapped open when she came in contact with the dressing on his arm. He was not wearing his sling. She had nearly forgotten how weak he still was. 'Michael, I…what are you doing?'

He raised up on his good arm so he could look at her. His lips curved in a slow smile that made her weak all over. 'Seducing you, my sweet. We are married, you know. I must perform certain duties as your husband to ensure your happiness. I thought I should start tonight.' He looked more deeply into her face. 'What is it? Am I going too fast for you? I promise I will be gentle. I won't hurt you.'

'It is not that. I might hurt you. You are still not well. Your aunt said you should not exert yourself.' She was finding it difficult to breathe—his touch was a drug, but she could not let him continue.

'She said you were to keep me confined to my bed as much as possible. It will be much easier for you if you are with me. Otherwise I shall be forced to trail you about the house.'

She stroked his beloved face with a gentle hand. 'But your wound, I do not want to aggravate it.'

He caught her hand and pressed it to his lips. His eyes were dark with passion. 'You won't hurt me. My love, I want to be with you tonight. I want to make love to you. I want to make you mine.' He cupped her face in his hands. 'Tell me that's what you want also. Tell me you love me as much as I love you.'

A small sound halfway between a sob and a laugh escaped her. 'I do love you, Michael.' And then he pressed her back against the pillows, his lips possessed hers, and his hands cupped her breasts through the soft fabric of her gown. She murmured a faint protest when he lifted his head but it was only to ease her nightdress over her head. Then there were no barriers between them.

The early light of dawn glimmered across the bed. Michael stirred and turned to wrap his arm more firmly around the soft warmth of the precious woman curled up against him. His wife. He liked the sound of that more than he'd ever imagined. Never had he dreamed union with a woman could be such a joining of soul and spirit as well as body.

She moved in his arms and he pressed his lips to the nape of her neck, burying his face in her silky tresses. She half-turned; her eyelids fluttered open. She looked at him with sleep-filled eyes.

'Good morning, my love.' He kissed her lightly. 'I hope you slept well.'

She gently caressed his face and returned his kiss.

'Yes, very well. Better than I have for weeks. But you, your arm, does it pain you?'

'A little, but I will survive.' He smiled, stroking the soft silky skin of her upper arm. 'I shall have to ensure you sleep well every night, then.' A delicate pink stained her cheeks. The shy modesty concealing her passionate nature intrigued and delighted him. 'So did last night persuade you marriage to me might be tolerable?'

'I shall have to see.'

'So you don't know yet? I can see I must try a little harder to convince you.' He shifted so his mouth and body covered hers. Her hands came up to pull his head to her.

Three-quarters of an hour later, Rosalyn lay with her head on his chest. He softly stroked her hair. 'What do you think now?' he inquired.

She smiled shyly. 'I think I shall find it much more than tolerable. In fact, I think I will like it very much.'

* * * * *

CHRISTMAS

Affairs

MORE THAN JUST KISSES UNDER THE MISTLETOE...

Enjoy three sparkling seasonal romances by your
favourite authors from

MILLS & BOON®
Presents™

HELEN BIANCHIN
For Anique, the season of goodwill has become...
The Seduction Season

SANDRA MARTON
Can Santa weave a spot of Christmas magic for Nick
and Holly in... *A Miracle on Christmas Eve*?

SHARON KENDRICK
Will Aleck and Clemmie have a... *Yuletide Reunion*?

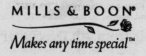

MILLS & BOON®
Makes any time special™

Available from 6th November 1998

4 FREE

books and a surprise gift!

We would like to take this opportunity to thank you for reading this Mills & Boon® book by offering you the chance to take FOUR more specially selected titles from the Historical Romance™ series absolutely FREE! We're also making this offer to introduce you to the benefits of the Reader Service™—

- ★ FREE home delivery
- ★ FREE gifts and competitions
- ★ FREE monthly Newsletter
- ★ Books available before they're in the shops
- ★ Exclusive Reader Service discounts

Accepting these FREE books and gift places you under no obligation to buy, you may cancel at any time, even after receiving your free shipment. Simply complete your details below and return the entire page to the address below. *You don't even need a stamp!*

YES! Please send me 4 free Historical Romance books and a surprise gift. I understand that unless you hear from me, I will receive 4 superb new titles every month for just £2.99 each, postage and packing free. I am under no obligation to purchase any books and may cancel my subscription at any time. The free books and gift will be mine to keep in any case.

H8YE

Ms/Mrs/Miss/Mr................................Initials ....
BLOCK CAPITALS PLEASE

Surname ....

Address ....

....

....Postcode................................

Send this whole page to:
THE READER SERVICE, FREEPOST, CROYDON, CR9 3WZ
(Eire readers please send coupon to: P.O. BOX 4546, DUBLIN 24.)

Offer not valid to current Reader Service subscribers to this series. We reserve the right to refuse an application and applicants must be aged 18 years or over. Only one application per household. Terms and prices subject to change without notice. Offer expires 31st May 1999. As a result of this application, you may receive further offers from Harlequin Mills & Boon and other carefully selected companies. If you would prefer not to share in this opportunity please write to The Data Manager, P.O. Box 236, Croydon, Surrey CR9 3RU.

Historical Romance is being used as a trademark.

mps
MAILING
PREFERENCE
SERVICE

MILLS & BOON®

*M*akes
any time
special

Enjoy a romantic novel from
Mills & Boon®

Presents™ *Enchanted*™ *Temptation*®

Historical Romance™ *Medical Romance*™